Our
Astonishing
Atmosphere

SCIENCE FOR  EVERYMAN

Our
Astonishing
Atmosphere

J. GORDON COOK

FELLOW OF THE ROYAL INSTITUTE OF CHEMISTS

THE DIAL PRESS   1957   NEW YORK

To MOLLY

MANUFACTURED IN THE UNITED STATES OF AMERICA

Preface

MOST of the land surface of the earth has now been explored by man. Already our twentieth-century explorers are seeking out new territories outside the earth itself. They are looking towards the mysterious worlds in the sky, reaching into space. But between us and the emptiness of space is a territory of which we still know comparatively little. This is the atmosphere, the ocean of gas that envelops the earth, and in which we live like insignificant creatures on the bottom of a vast but flimsy sea.

The exploration of our atmosphere is now going on apace. Science has given us machines and instruments that enable us to reach for information high above the earth, and much has been discovered in the last few years.

In this book I have summarized information that is now available about our atmosphere. Each chapter deals with a different aspect of the air in its relation to everyday life.

J. GORDON COOK

Contents

Illustrations

1

Blanket over the Earth

THE fog lies damp and heavy as it drifts slowly over the town. Islands of feeble light loom and disappear as we grope our way homeward along the pavement. A siren booms from a ship moving warily down the river.

On days like this we notice the air in which we live. As we cough and splutter in the smoky fog we realize once again that the air is as vital to us as our food. Then the fog lifts and the sun comes out. The air is sweet, and we forget it again.

Yet we should not forget. Much of the beauty of life comes from the air. The deep blue of a summer sky is painted by sunlight scattered in the particles of the air. The rosy dawn and the flaming sunset come from light that is bent as it skims the air on the surface of the earth.

Without air there could be no life as we know it to-day. Baked by the blistering sun during the day, the earth would be scorched without air to filter and soften the sunshine. At night, with no blanket of air to hold back its warmth, the earth would shiver in arctic frosts.

Every day millions of meteors disintegrate in the upper layers of our atmosphere. Without its shield of air the land would be barren and pocked by a myriad craters under this constant bombardment from space.

The life built up on earth uses air as a reservoir of essential fuels and foods. To the animal world, air means oxygen that can be breathed to 'burn up' food in the body; to plants, air provides carbon dioxide from which most of the substances of life are made.

Though we cannot see it or hold it, the air is a material thing no less than the water or rocks of the earth. But its particles roam freely and independently as a gas, instead of huddling close to one another as they do in a liquid or solid. The air, like other matter, has weight. A column of air weighing nearly half a ton rests on the head of each one of us. Altogether the earth's atmosphere contains 5000 million million tons of air. Four-fifths of this great ocean of gas is nitrogen; the rest is mainly oxygen, with traces of carbon dioxide, water vapour, and other gases making up less than a hundredth of the whole.

Only the force of gravity holds this mass of air on the surface of the earth. Without it the gases would stream off into space and join the wandering gases of the Milky Way. In the upper layers of the atmosphere there is a slow, steady leakage of air into space by particles moving so quickly that they can overcome the gravitational attraction of the earth. But scientists have estimated that it will take more than a million million million million million million million years for the earth to lose all its oxygen and nitrogen in this way. So there is little need to worry unduly about it yet.

Although it is convenient to think of our atmosphere as a well-defined layer of gas that blankets the surface of the earth, it is really impossible to say where the air disappears and space begins. The air becomes thinner and thinner as we rise higher and higher above the earth. At sea-level the particles of gas are crowded closely together, but they thin out steadily as the altitude increases. At 10,000 feet the air is thin enough to make breathing uncomfortable. At 20,000 feet human beings cannot live unless they have become acclimatized. And at 40,000 feet there is only sufficient air to allow us to remain conscious for a few seconds.

Although we know that there are still appreciable numbers of atmospheric gas particles 600 miles above the earth, the thinning out of the air is so rapid that the layer of air below 20,000 feet contains more than half the total weight of the atmosphere. There is more air lying below the summit of Mount Everest than there is in the hundreds of miles of atmosphere above it. By the time we reach up two or three hundred miles into the atmosphere the particles of air are so far apart that they are more sparse than the gas particles in the vacuum of a television tube.

For every million particles of gas in the air at sea-level there is only one at a height of 60 miles. At sea-level the particles are packed together so closely that each particle can travel, on average, only a few millionths of an inch before bumping into another one. At a height of 60 miles the distance travelled between collisions has extended to an inch; and at a height of 800 miles there are so few particles that each one will travel 2000 miles before it bumps into its neighbour.

With little of the earth's surface left to be explored, we have begun to concentrate more seriously on exploration in the atmosphere. The air is a frontier separating us from the greater mystery of space. Although human beings have reached only comparatively low altitudes, balloons and rockets are carrying scientific equipment hundreds of miles into the air. Our knowledge of the upper atmosphere is coming from observations made in this way, from the study of atmospheric phenomena such as the aurora borealis, and from the reflection of sound and wireless waves by different layers of the air.

As we rise from the ground the air becomes gradually cooler. At a height of about seven miles the temperature has fallen to almost $-67°F$. It then becomes steady, remaining at this temperature as the height increases. This levelling out of the air temperature marks the boundary between two regions of the atmosphere. The lower layer, in which the air becomes colder with increasing height, is called the troposphere. The layer above it, in which the air maintains a steady temperature, is the stratosphere.

The height of the boundary between the troposphere and the stratosphere varies with the general movement of the air below it. It is highest over the tropics, reaching eleven miles, and lowest over the poles, where it is only three or four miles high. The air of the stratosphere also steadies at different temperatures, depending on its situation over the earth. It is coldest at the tropics at $-112°$F., and warmest over the poles at $-67°$F. The troposphere, extending up to seven or eight miles over temperate latitudes, is the layer of the atmosphere whose behaviour concerns us most directly here on earth. This is the layer which gives us our weather. It is packed with the water vapour that causes clouds and rain and fog; in it the air moves to and fro, carrying the water vapour from one place to another in a constant turmoil of wind and weather.

In the stratosphere the air becomes calm and still. Most of the moisture has been left behind, and there is little dust and dirt. The air in the stratosphere is crisp and dry and clear. There are no clouds or storms. With few particles in the air to scatter the light the blue of the sky begins to disappear as we enter the stratosphere. In the lower layers at eight or nine miles high the sky has changed to violet. Then farther up the sky becomes black with the blackness of space. The stars appear, and the sun glares down like a burning torch held in the dark, unfriendly sky.

As we rise still farther into the stratosphere the temperature once again begins to change. The air grows warmer, until at a height of 30 miles it reaches 170°F. This is the region of a warm belt in the stratosphere. Higher still the air becomes cooler again, the temperature dropping to −117°F. at 50 miles.

This layer of warm air in the stratosphere coincides with a rise in the amount of ozone in the air. Ozone is a form of oxygen in which the atoms join together in threes instead of in the usual pairs. It is formed from oxygen by the action of the ultra-violet rays from the sun. These dangerous, burning rays are absorbed by the ozone in the stratosphere layer, shielding the earth from an overdose of sunshine. Without the ozone layer, life would be frizzled up by the intense radiations.

In the air at ground-level there is only the merest trace of ozone. Even at the seaside, where ozone is often regarded as part and parcel of the bracing air, there is virtually none. One part of ozone in a million parts of air can be dangerous to human beings; if the warm layer of the stratosphere was compressed to sea-level pressure the concentration of ozone in it would be lethal.

Although the lower levels of the stratosphere are calm and still, there are often violent winds blowing in the upper layers. Meteors flying through these high-level layers of air leave trails of dust behind them as they disintegrate. By watching these trails we can see how the air is moving in the upper atmosphere. Sometimes the meteor trails take up a zigzag shape as they pass through layers of air moving rapidly in different directions. Calculations have shown that a meteor can pass through a wind blowing at 100 miles an hour in one direction, only to meet a wind moving equally fast in the opposite direction half a mile lower down.

These streams of moving air at heights of 50 miles or more are probably caused by the warm ozone-rich layer which reaches its peak at about 30 miles. The general tendency seems to be for air above 50 miles to move eastwards at over 100 miles an hour, with the layer below drifting slowly westward.

Above this level, in the upper stratosphere, the air begins to undergo drastic changes which characterize the third and uppermost level of the atmosphere. The radiations from the sun have begun to break up the individual particles of gas into smaller particles which may be electrically charged. The air is in an excited state, and electrical currents can flow through it just as they can flow through the rarefied gas in a neon tube. At a height of about 55 miles we leave the stratosphere and enter the ionosphere.

This change from the stratosphere to the ionosphere is in fact a gradual one. The break-up of the gases into electrically charged particles begins at as low as 30 miles. But at 55 miles the air has become sufficiently affected to be able to reflect radio waves back to earth. This is the Heaviside Layer, and is usually taken as the lower level of the ionosphere. Above it the air becomes the plaything of the radiations and emanations reaching us from space. Inside the ionosphere the gases flicker and glow with auroral light under the effect of electric and magnetic influences.

As we emerge from the protective shield of the atmospheric gases, rising higher and higher into the ionosphere, the tenuous gases become warmer. At a height of 250 miles the temperature has reached more than 4000°F. But in air so thin, temperature becomes meaningless in the sense that we understand it at ground-level. As the air increases in temperature its individual particles are becoming more agitated. They move more violently to and fro, and the temperature is a measure of the violence of their agitation. Warmth is felt by a human being in this air as a result of the bombardment of its particles. But 250 miles up in the atmosphere there are so few of these over-excited particles that they would pass on little warmth to anyone who was there. Much more important would be the direct effect of radiation from the sun. Unprotected by the blanket of air that covers us at sea-level, we should be roasted on the sunny side and frozen solid on the other.

In these upper reaches of the atmosphere the mixture of gases forming the air has undergone a number of changes. The low-level air of the troposphere alters little from one place to another. Always nitrogen makes up four-fifths of it, oxygen about one-fifth, with carbon dioxide and other gases making up a small fraction of the whole. Only the amount of water vapour varies, entering and leaving the air continually as it takes part in the vagaries of the weather. Any local variations in the proportions of the other gases, caused, for example, by animal or vegetable life, are quickly smoothed out by the constant turbulence of the troposphere. But in the ionosphere the air is not protected from the effects of solar radiation. Chemical changes take place. Gases such as hydrogen appear in unusually large amounts, possibly fed into the outer air as emanations from the sun itself. And in exchange there is a continual loss of particles by leakage into space.

Our knowledge of the air in these far-away levels of the atmosphere is necessarily limited. But research rockets are reaching ever higher into the air, and are already probing tentatively at the boundaries of space.

Throughout the year all sorts of influences play upon the air, keeping it in a state of movement and turbulence. The earth itself drags the air along as it rotates about its axis. The sun heats the earth and air more strongly in the tropics than at the poles, causing vast movements of the air across the surface of the earth. The land and sea warm up unevenly in the sun and cool at different rates. Above them the air moves to and fro in a constant and unavailing struggle to smooth out the pressure differences.

Always the air is on the move. Over hills it flows, and down into the valleys; it becomes hotter and picks up moisture from the land and over the sea and deposits it again as rain or fog or snow. It is this great mix-up of our air that brings the ever-changing weather to every country in the world. Sometimes the air moves gently as it swishes through the waving corn; sometimes it rampages across the earth, uprooting homes and trees, whirling them into the funnel of a raging tornado.

Although our winds blow warm and then cold, switching from one direction to another from hour to hour, there is an overall pattern in the flow of air over the earth as a whole. The local whorls and eddies that bring such rapid changes in the weather are like the little currents and whirlpools that break up the flow of water in a river. These great wind movements have been mapped and studied since man began to venture across the seas in sailing ships. Wind was the power that pushed our ships about the world for centuries. The sea has helped us to build up a great wealth of information about the winds that blow over different areas of the earth.

In tropical regions the air moves more steadily than in temperate latitudes. Near the equator itself is the region of great calm where the air lies still and heavy. These are the doldrums, where ships lay becalmed for weeks or even months without a breath of air to fill their sails.

North and south of the doldrums lie the great belts of winds blowing obliquely towards the equator. These trade winds blow from a north-easterly direction; in the Southern Hemisphere they blow south-easterly.

Above the trade wind belt in the Northern Hemisphere lies another great region of general wind movement blowing in the opposite direction. These winds are the westerlies, which sweep over the North Atlantic from America towards the coast of Europe. These are the warm, wet winds that blow over Britain, bringing the rain that is rarely away for long.

Between the two opposing systems, the Trades and the westerlies, lies another belt of calm air called the horse latitudes. This was the region where mariners so often had to lighten ship by throwing their horses overboard. Above the westerlies the wind changes again to north-easterly as it blows near the Arctic Circle.

These great wind systems, the Trades, the westerlies, and the arctic winds, represent the movement of air in the lowest levels of the atmosphere. When the world's transport system remained at sea-level they were the winds that counted. But as we took to the air, and flying became an established means of transport and travel, the movement of winds in the upper layers of air became gradually more important. Meteorology had to extend its investigations to the upper air. And as techniques have developed for ' sounding ' at high level we have found that the movement of air in the upper layers of the troposphere and in the stratosphere are very different from the wind movements near the surface of the earth.

These upper-air winds are of interest not only to people who must fly through them. They help to determine the sort of weather that we suffer down below. Movements in the upper air have a tremendous influence on the behaviour of the air near the earth's surface.

Much of our information about the air in the upper layers of the troposphere comes from meteorological balloons. From stations scattered all over the Northern Hemisphere hydrogen-filled balloons are sent up every day to heights of as much as 50,000 feet. Behind them these balloons trail meteorological equipment that radios information back to earth about the air through which it is rising. Since the end of World War II balloons have been used to follow wind movements. Carrying special radar-reflecting materials, the balloons soar up into the air and are followed by radar as they are blown along by winds in the upper air.

Information about the movements of the upper air has accumulated until we can now make out general wind patterns in the higher levels of the troposphere. They differ radically from those near the surface of the earth.

For forty years or more British meteorologists have known that balloons are often whipped suddenly away by winds blowing violently at heights of up to seven or eight miles. But until modern techniques made possible a detailed study of these winds little was known about them other than the fact that they existed.

Shortly before World War II meteorologists at the Massachusetts Institute of Technology confirmed that fast-moving winds were blowing near the base of the stratosphere. These winds appeared to blow as long, curving ribbons of moving air that snaked round the earth between 10,000 and 50,000 feet.

At that time information about the upper air was sketchy and sparse. But with the outbreak of war every effort was made to increase our knowledge of meteorological conditions. Weather forecasting was of supreme importance to the Allied war effort, and a network of stations was established over much of the Northern Hemisphere, with upper-air soundings as an essential function of each station. Soon it was confirmed that this fast-moving ribbon of air existed high up in the troposphere. It has since been given the name of the 'jet stream.'

When American planes began the high-level bombarding of Japan in 1943 they had first-hand experience of the jet stream. Pilots reported that during bombing runs at 30,000 feet their planes were standing still by relation with the ground. The air in which they were flying was moving at as much as 300 miles an hour in the direction opposite to that of the planes. When the planes turned homeward they were borne along at twice their normal speed.

After the War intensive research was begun to find out more about the jet stream. The basic facts about it have now been established, but many more years of investigation will be needed before the finer points of its behaviour are understood.

Almost the entire layer of the troposphere above 10,000 feet is moving in a westerly direction over the Northern Hemisphere. In tropical latitudes the movement is slow, but as we move northward the wind increases in speed until it reaches its maximum somewhere between the Tropic of Cancer and the Arctic Circle. Then the speed tails off again towards the pole. The region of maximum speed coincides with what we call the jet stream.

Usually the wind forming the jet stream blows fastest just below the stratosphere, at about 30,000 feet. The air movement slows down at lower levels until, by 10,000 feet, it is blowing at only a quarter of the speed it attains in the stream itself.

In the neighbourhood of the jet stream the air moves along in the form of narrow jets that converge to form the main stream, like tributaries running into a river. Speeds often reach up to 300 miles an hour. In winter the stream flows for thousands of miles, girdling the earth over the Tropic of Cancer. In summer it moves up towards the Arctic Circle.

Flowing on its winter course, the jet stream moves faster than it does during the summer. Its peak speeds are reached as it leaves the coast of Asia and begins its journey over the Pacific, and across the bulge of Africa towards India.

Although these great circumpolar paths represent the overall movement of the jet stream as it roars round the earth, the stream meanders to and fro like a huge snake over vast areas of the earth. Its path will undulate as it sweeps down towards the equator for two or three thousand miles, only to turn up in a huge curve and swing back towards the pole. Up and down it goes, tracing a wave-like path round the world.

These undulations of the jet stream are of the greatest importance in their effects on the weather. They cause the out-of-season variations in the weather that can bring a sudden heat-wave in the autumn or a long spell of frost and snow in spring.

The jet stream flows along the edge of the great mass of cold air that covers the pole. North of the stream the air is cold; south of it is the air that has been warmed up by the tropical sun. The jet stream makes a moving boundary between the two in the upper air. Below it, a few hundred miles farther south, is the polar front, the corresponding boundary in the lower layer of the troposphere.

When the jet stream starts to meander up and down it drags huge lobes of polar air into lower altitudes, with corresponding lobes of warm air reaching up towards the pole. Eventually, after following this undulating course perhaps for weeks, the jet stream returns to its more direct route round the earth, cutting across the base of the lobes of polar air and leaving them as huge, cold pools lying over thousands of square miles of land. Farther north the upward-reaching lobes of tropical air are left by way of compensation.

This switching of enormous pools of air between the polar regions and the tropics is nature's way of mixing and modifying the air that covers the earth. If we knew more about the jet stream that girdles and contains the polar air we should be able to increase the efficiency of our weather forecasting.

During the War, as information accumulated about conditions in the upper air, a start was made on long-range forecasting. In 1940 experimental five-day forecasts were being made, and month-ahead predictions were started soon afterwards. This type of long-range forecasting of weather trends was of the greatest value in military planning; in the United States it has become an established peace-time activity.

The modern network of meteorological stations that covers Europe and North America has enabled meteorologists to keep in touch with the course of the jet stream as it meanders through the air of the Northern Hemisphere. Facts have accumulated, and our understanding of the vagaries of the jet stream is enabling meteorologists to predict its behaviour with increasing accuracy. Over the Atlantic the balloons sent up by the weather ships provide sufficient information to keep track of the jet stream as it crosses from America to Europe. But over vast expanses of the Pacific the jet stream wanders at will without our knowing what has happened to it.

In the Southern Hemisphere meteorological information is sparse, and little is known about conditions in the upper air. But sufficient is now known to show that a southern jet stream girdles the South Pole, flowing from a westerly direction.

To aircraft pilots interest in the jet stream is not confined to its help in predicting weather more accurately. If the position of the stream was known with accuracy it would be possible for a pilot to increase his speed by as much as 300 miles an hour when flying in the same direction as the stream. And by keeping clear of the stream when flying in the opposite direction he could be sure that he did not 'stand still' in the air until his fuel ran out.

Unfortunately, there are difficulties in flying with the jet stream which will probably minimize its practical use. Pilots have flown into areas of severe turbulence in the jet stream region. Without warning, their planes are bumped about as though by a giant hammer. These areas of turbulence are often 100 miles wide and nearly a mile thick.

Although scientists have tried to find an explanation for the jet stream, no theory has yet been able to explain all the facts about it in a satisfactory way. Much remains to be found out about its finer structure, about the narrow filaments of air that come together to form the main stream itself. But this is no easy task. Even the main jet stream is often less than 200 miles wide, and to follow its track as it winds through thousands of square miles of air is possible only by maintaining a dense network of sounding stations.

As our knowledge and understanding of the jet stream becomes more precise, so it will become possible to predict with greater accuracy the trends in the weather for weeks and even months ahead.

2

The Wind goes to Work

In the endless movements of the air the world has unlimited supplies of potential power. Energy is poured
into the atmosphere from the sun; it is the fuel that
keeps the trade winds and the westerlies blowing, and
hurricanes and tornadoes roaring over the earth. By
ordinary human standards the amount of energy available in the moving air is fantastically large. We think
of atom bombs as impressive energy-liberating devices.
But a thousand atom bombs a minute would not provide
the energy that is locked up in a modest gale.

The world to-day is desperately short of energy
supplies. We need energy to provide the power that
drives our factories and mills, our trains and cars and
planes. We need it to heat our homes and, in the form
of food, to keep us all alive. Yet we make little use of
the vast amounts of energy available to us in the wind.
We no longer expect it to carry us across the seas; we
have almost abandoned it as a help in grinding corn.
Only in small, isolated places, in farms and homesteads,
do we find the wind being put to work, pumping water
or driving small electric generators. For many years
men have talked of harnessing the power of the wind.
But in industrial countries such as Britain, Germany,
or the United States—all great energy-users—alternative sources of power have been too readily available.
Coal, oil, and water have supplied much of the power
that has been demanded since the Industrial Revolution

created such a need for something that would turn the factory wheels.

In recent years the price of coal in Britain has rocketed; as a consequence, the cost of everything we make from coal has risen. Electricity, generated from the energy liberated by burning coal in the power station, has become so expensive that any alternative method of producing it is worth attention. And at last the wind is coming into its own as a potential source of power.

Every day, when the winds drift in from the Atlantic, millions of horse-powers blow over the west coast of Britain. There is enough power in this mass of moving air to provide us with all the power we need. Research carried out already indicates that, with the help of relatively few wind machines, we could derive at least as much energy from this source as we could get from water-power. This energy could be fed as electricity into the grid—the network of cables that carries electricity from our power stations to places all over Britain. And for every unit of electricity contributed by the wind we should save up to 1½ lb. of coal.

A Wind Power Committee was set up in Britain in 1948 to assess the possibilities of drawing on our supplies of wind-power. Since that time great progress has been made, and two large windmill generators have been built.

Although the total energy stored up in the wind is so enormous, it is not a simple matter to draw on this energy and put it to practical use. If it had been, we should have been using wind energy long ago.

Compared with water, the air is tenuous and thin. It takes a great volume of air to yield a useful amount of energy. A small propeller or turbine driven round by water flowing from a reservoir can generate a lot of electricity; but a tremendous propeller is needed to draw as much energy from the moving wind. The old windmills carried massive sails to drive comparatively small grindstones in the mill.

Added to this difficulty there is the variability of the wind. The air is rarely flowing steadily from one direction; it blows in gusts, changing speed and direction from one minute to the next. Nor is there any guarantee that the wind will blow at all. The air will often lie still and calm for days on end. A windmill operating on its own can never be relied upon to provide a steady supply of power; it is of only limited use under modern living conditions.

Wind-power generators tend to be considered, therefore, as a means of supplementing the existing power supplies. They can never take the place of the coal-burning power stations in Britain; but they could feed a supply of electricity into the grid when the wind was blowing well, enabling us to save our coal.

Since the Wind Power Committee was set up in Britain in 1948, scientists have surveyed the country to find sites that are suitable for wind-power generators. To operate economically, generators of convenient size would need an average wind-speed of at least 20 miles an hour. Meteorological charts based on records going back for many years show that this is higher than the average speeds over any large region of Great Britain. On the extreme west coast the average wind-speed is 16 to 18 miles an hour; a little farther inland it drops to 14 to 16 miles an hour. But within these regions there are isolated spots where local conditions create a higher-than-average wind-speed throughout the year. A gently rising slope, for example, can speed up the wind flowing over it like the curved surface of an aeroplane wing. The wind is forced to travel a longer distance as it flows over the hill; it is moving faster than the rest of the air as it reaches the summit.

Some eighty sites have been selected in Britain where wind-speeds are high enough throughout the year to operate a windmill generator. On some of the sites the average wind-speed is half as fast again as the wind in the surrounding regions. Ten of the sites have wind-speeds of almost 30 m.p.h.; in most of the others the average wind-speed is more than 20 m.p.h.

Many of the selected sites are on the summits of gently sloping hills where the ground rises steadily without any serious irregularities to cause air turbulence. There are sites in Cornwall and the Shetlands, in Northern Ireland, and even places in the east of Britain. It has been estimated that there are some hundreds of suitable sites in Britain altogether.

Many of the sites have been surveyed by scientists who have checked the wind-speeds over many months. Local farmers and shepherds have given invaluable help as temporary technicians through the year, checking the readings of scientific instruments set on lonely hill-tops.

Although the day-to-day vagaries of the wind can be so irritating to the engineer who has to design a windmill generator, the wind blows remarkably steady throughout the year as a whole. The total quantity of air that drifts across a site varies little from year to year; it is more constant than the rainfall. A generator could be relied upon to produce its quota of electricity during the year.

In order to operate economically, the wind generator has to be able to take the energy from a large volume of moving air. Modern generators use a huge propeller, with two or three great blades thrashing through an area of hundreds of square feet. These windmills are æsthetically less attractive than their gently moving predecessors, but they are more efficient. The propeller is mounted at the top of a steel pylon or tower, often with the electric generator immediately behind it. In

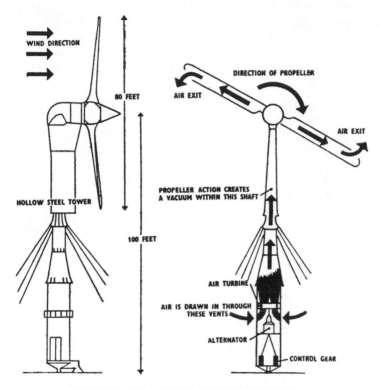

WIND DIRECTION

80 FEET

HOLLOW STEEL TOWER

100 FEET

DIRECTION OF PROPELLER

AIR EXIT

AIR EXIT

PROPELLER ACTION CREATES A VACUUM WITHIN THIS SHAFT

AIR TURBINE

AIR IS DRAWN IN THROUGH THESE VENTS

ALTERNATOR

CONTROL GEAR

DIAGRAM OF A WIND-DRIVEN DYNAMO

This shows how air is drawn through the hollow steel tower
of the windmill, driving a turbine coupled to the generator.

By courtesy of Enfield Cables, Ltd

principle the operation of the windmill is as simple as it
was when its job was grinding corn. The propeller is
driven round by the wind, turning the dynamo behind
it to generate electricity.

Building a windmill of this type, however, presents
a host of technical difficulties. Designed to catch and
draw the energy from the wind, it must yet be able to
withstand gusts and gales of 100 m.p.h. or more.

The first successful windmill to generate power commercially was built in America during the early years
of World War II. On a hill in Vermont, called Grandpa's
Knob, a huge steel pylon was built, carrying a two-
bladed propeller measuring 130 feet from tip to tip.
Behind the propeller, also on the top of the tower, was
the generating plant.

In October 1941 the blades of this huge windmill
began to turn. The electricity generated was fed into a
public supply system serving 5000 people. For nearly
four years the wind generator worked spasmodically.
All sorts of technical problems developed and were put
right. By February 1945 the teething troubles had been
overcome and the mill was working smoothly. For three
weeks it supplied its quota of electricity without a hitch.
Then, on March 26, 1945, a strong wind began to rock
the tower and the strain became too great. One of the
8-ton blades broke away at the root and was flung more
than 200 yards from the tower. After this the project
was abandoned. It had been a costly experiment, but
it was not entirely a worthless one. It had proved that
the wind could be persuaded to release its energy and
provide electric power on a commercial scale.

In the United States, where ample supplies of coal,
oil, and water-power are available, the urge to make
practical use of the wind is not very intense. But in
Britain, as in many other countries, the natural resources
of stored energy are not so lavish, and there is a greater

incentive to push ahead with the development of wind machines.

With the survey of sites well under way, British engineers built the first large power windmill for the North of Scotland Hydro-electric Board at Costa Hill, in the Orkney Islands. Like the machine built in Vermont, this one consists of a steel pylon carrying a propeller and generating plant on top. It is smaller than the American windmill; the tower is 80 feet high, and the propeller has three blades, each 30 feet in length. The power output is 100 kilowatts, compared with 1250 kilowatts of the windmill on Grandpa's Knob. It is regarded as an experimental machine that will provide information on which much larger windmills can be designed.

At St Albans, in Hertfordshire, the second British power windmill has been built, using a radically different design. This windmill is mounted on a 100-ft. tower which is in the form of a huge steel tube. The two aluminium blades of the windmill are hollow, and each has a hole near the tip. The hollow blades are connected to the tubular tower through a hollow axle, forming a continuous pipe through which air can flow.

As the blades revolve air inside them is thrown towards the tips by centrifugal force, just as the riders on a roundabout tend to be thrown towards the edge. As it reaches the tips of the blades the air escapes through the holes, creating a vacuum inside the blades and down through the tower. This vacuum sucks air in from vents under the base of the tower.

When the blades revolve air rushes in a continuous stream into the vents, up through the tower and hollow axle, and into the blades, until it is finally flung out through the holes in the blade tips. Moving up through the tower, this stream of air blows past a smaller windmill in the form of a turbine, which, in turn, drives an electric generator in the base of the tower. There is an obvious advantage in having the generator at the bottom of the tower instead of the top.

The St Albans windmill was built as a joint effort by three companies, including the De Havilland Aircraft Company, Ltd, who built the Comet airliner. The revolutionary principle of the windmill was proposed by a French motor engineer, and the design of the propeller owes much to aeronautical experience. The aluminium blades, similar in size to the wings of the Comet, were made at the De Havilland factory at Hatfield, near London.

Incorporated into both these experimental British windmills are devices for controlling the speed of the propellers. The blades are feathered automatically to suit the speed of the wind, keeping the mill rotating at a constant speed. If the winds are too high the blades of the St Albans windmill can 'flap' instead of presenting a rigid surface to the full force of the wind.

These two British windmills will provide much of the knowledge for building future mills, possibly of much greater capacity and with propellers up to 200 ft. in length. Other experimental windmills are under test in Denmark, France, and Germany.

To be able to feed current into the public supply system these mills must be able to rotate at constant speed and generate current at suitable frequency. They must be able to stand up to gales and storms and yet be able to wring every unit of energy from a gentle breeze. They must be reasonably cheap to build and maintain, and should be able to operate with a minimum of attention.

On factors like these will depend the cost of the electricity that is generated by the windmills. There is no fuel to pay for once the mill is turning. If capital cost, depreciation, and maintenance can be kept to a minimum, the electricity will be cheap enough to make power windmills an economic proposition.

Research has so far indicated that windmills with outputs reaching 4000 kilowatts will probably be an economic size under British conditions. Large generators of this type could produce electricity at a cost lower than that from modern coal-burning power stations. A network of these windmills on sites already selected could provide enough electricity to save four million tons of coal a year.

In an industrial country like Britain, with a highly organized system of electricity supply, the emphasis in wind-power research is towards this type of large windmill. It would be a supplementary source of power. But in many parts of the world there is a lively interest in the windmill as an independent power generator. Countries like Burma and India are at a stage of industrial development where cheap power has become an essential need. Often there are no coal or water-power resources, and fuel must be carried long distances to the power stations. Electricity then becomes too expensive for wide-scale use.

Over many of these countries the wind is carrying all the energy that they could use, if only it could be tapped economically.

Where the windmill has to act as the main source of electricity its greatest drawback lies in the fluctuating supply. When the wind dies down the power supply peters out. But there are ways of overcoming this difficulty, and their investigation is part and parcel of the effort that is now being put into making use of wind power.

Where a windmill is feeding electricity to a small community it can be run in conjunction with a diesel generator. When the wind dies down the diesel engine takes over.

The energy developed by the windmill can be stored in various ways. Electricity can itself be stored in accumulators, as it is in a car. But batteries are cumbersome and expensive; they are costly to maintain and of little use for really large-scale work.

Electricity generated when the wind is blowing well can be stored indirectly. Passed through water, it will split the water into oxygen and hydrogen gases. The hydrogen gas can then be stored and burned as fuel or used to drive an engine. Surplus electricity can also be used for boiling water, and the steam stored and drawn upon to provide heat and power when the air is still. Or the electricity can be made to pump water into a storage tank or reservoir at a higher level, turning itself into a source of hydro-electric power.

Whenever energy is switched about in this way from one form to another some of it is lost. It is always best to use the electricity direct from the generator if this is possible. But the 'amenity' value of electricity is so high in many parts of the world that storage systems for wind power could be an economic proposition.

Photo "Picture Post"

CIRRUS CLOUDS AND THE JET STREAM

Clouds like this are a sign that the jet stream is racing overhead.

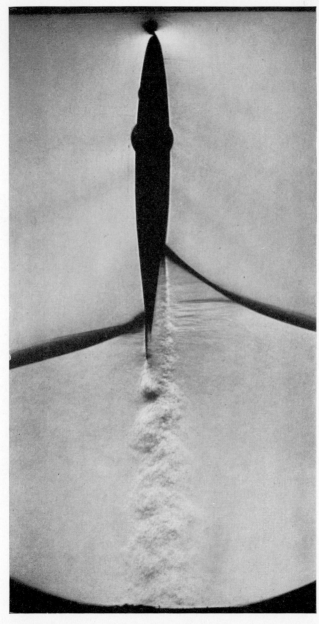

Photo National Physical Laboratory. Crown copyright reserved

AIR COMPRESSION WAVES

This photograph, taken in a high-speed wind tunnel, shows the shock-waves formed as air flows past a model
aircraft wing at almost the speed of sound.

3

Faster and Higher

ON December 17, 1903, Orville Wright, watched by his brother, Wilbur, and nine other spectators, began our twentieth-century conquest of the air. In a rickety, ramshackle plane, powered by a home-made engine developing twelve horse-power, he flew for twelve seconds at a speed of 30 miles an hour. Now, little more than half a century later, man has flown at over a thousand miles an hour, and the prospect of even more fantastic speeds is well in sight.

Before the Wright brothers made their historic flight over the field at Kitty Hawk they were confronted by technical problems that they worked out for themselves, largely by trial and error. The aircraft industry which has followed them has established itself on a solid foundation of scientific research. The modern designer has a background of mathematics and aerodynamics to help him when he plans his plane. But within recent years, as aircraft have begun to fly at speeds in the region of 500 to 600 miles an hour, new problems have cropped up. The aerodynamics that served well enough when men were content to fly at two or three hundred miles an hour are inadequate as these higher speeds are reached. The air through which the plane must fly begins to play unexpected tricks; controls are affected and resistance to the flight of the plane increases at a startling rate.

These new problems are associated with our approach

to flying at the speed of sound. They are a result of fundamental changes in the behaviour of the air through which the plane must force its way.

When a plane flies through the air at ' normal ' speeds the molecules of oxygen, nitrogen, and other gases forming the air are pushed out of the way of the wings and fuselage without great difficulty. They flow along past the moving plane and join up with their neighbours again as they reach the end of the plane's tail. This smooth flow of air is encouraged by streamlining, a rounded front moving the air smoothly aside to make room for the narrowing tail. Any molecules of air that are bumped by the moving plane at these relatively low speeds are able to move away at a speed of about 760 miles an hour at sea-level. This is the speed at which pressure pulses travel through the air—the speed of sound.

In this way a plane that is flying at two or three hundred miles an hour sends a warning of its approach to the air ahead, which prepares to take avoiding action in good time. But as the speed increases the air is given less and less time to move aside, and by the time that the plane is moving at the speed of sound the molecules of air that are buffeted by it are unable to get out of the way before the plane is on top of them. At sonic speeds a layer of tight-packed air molecules is built up in front of the fuselage and leading edges of the plane's wings. There is a wall of tightly compressed air barring the plane's passage. Instead of being able to thrust its way smoothly through the air, the plane has to force its way against this pressure wall, pushing the mass of air violently to the side as it forges ahead.

This pressure wall is the phenomenon that is often called the sound barrier. It is built up by a plane at speeds within the region of the speed of sound itself, and its effects can be alarming. As the plane increases its speed still further, reaching into the supersonic region of, say, 1200 to 1500 miles an hour, the barrier disappears. The molecules of air are knocked away at a speed much faster than they can normally travel, and they are swept aside and left to trail along behind.

Although planes have now penetrated this sound barrier many times, designers find great difficulty in producing power units that can maintain a plane in level flight at the speed of sound. Supersonic flying is achieved with the help of rocket propulsion or by calling in the assistance of gravity. A jet plane flying at 50,000 feet, for example, will dive to 25,000 feet, pushing through the sound barrier on its way. We are not at present concerned with the problem of providing regular airline services in planes that have to cope with the sound barrier. But the effects of air moving at sonic speeds is of vital practical importance in another way.

When planes began to fly at speeds approaching 500 miles an hour pilots found that strange things happened. The plane began to lose its power to lift, and the propellers lost some of their normal efficiency. Although the plane itself was travelling at a speed well below the speed of sound, these effects were due to compression areas built up by air flowing over the plane at sonic speeds.

The air flowing past a bulging cockpit canopy, for example, must travel a longer route from the front to the back of the plane than air flowing smoothly over a flat surface. It is like a runner who is handicapped by having to run from point to point over a curved track; he must run faster than an opponent running over a direct track between the same points.

In a similar way the air flowing past a rounded surface on a plane is forced to travel faster than the actual speed of the plane itself. This effect can make the air travel at the speed of sound when the plane is moving at speeds in the region of 500 miles an hour. Just as the forward movement of a plane at sonic speeds will build up a pressure wall in front of it, so will this air speed-up in slower-moving planes create compression areas alongside the plane. The effect is particularly serious on the wings.

The wings of a normal subsonic plane are thick at the front and taper away towards the rear. The upper surface is curved deliberately to force the air moving over it to take a longer route. This means not only that the air molecules must move faster over it, but that they are spaced out more thinly than the molecules taking the route below the wing. As the pressure of the air on anything is caused by the bumping of continually agitated molecules, the pressure above the wing is less than it is below. So the wing and the plane are lifted into the air by the more numerous molecules bumping against the underside.

When the speed of the plane is in the region of 500 m.p.h. the air moving by the long route over the top of the wing may reach the speed of sound. And once again the pile-up begins. Molecules of air are pushed up against each other so fast that they have not time to get out of the way. Above the wing a compression area is formed and the lift of the wings is seriously affected.

In a similar way the formation of a compression area cuts down the efficiency of a fast-moving propeller. In modern planes approaching sonic speeds the propeller revolves at terrific speed. In the centre, near the hub, the rate at which the blade is moving may be comparatively slow, but the tips of the blades can be cutting through the air at sonic speeds. When this happens the formation of a compression barrier influences the flow of air past the spinning blade, and the propeller loses power.

These effects, which occur at sustained speeds within

the capabilities of modern planes, are having a drastic influence on modern aircraft design. To cut down the loss of lift and control, wings are being made thinner. The introduction of the jet engine for high-speed flight has largely overcome the difficulties associated with the propellers.

In planes which are designed to fly at the speed of sound, and even faster, the problems become still more acute. To enable the plane to thrust its wings and fuselage through the compression wall the frontal area is cut down as far as possible. The streamlined pear-drop shape, so efficient at low speeds, must be discarded. In place of the blunt, rounded nose which piles up air in front of it, the supersonic plane has a pointed nose. The advantage of this was discovered at the end of the nineteenth century, even before the first plane had flown. Experiments carried out with shells and bullets had shown that they flew more efficiently through the air when given pointed noses.

The wings of a supersonic plane are made to present the smallest possible area as the plane moves forward. The rounded leading-edge of the subsonic plane gives way to the thin knife edge that can cut its way through the wall of air, and to make things easier still the wings are small, sweeping back at a sharp angle like an arrowhead.

Plunging through the air at sonic speeds, a plane of this shape can burst its way through the compression wall it creates. Behind it, sweeping out at an angle like the wake of a ship, is a region of still-compressed air forming what is called the shock-wave.

As the speed of the plane increases still further into the supersonic region, things begin to alter once again. The air is thrust aside so abruptly that it is given no time to build its pressure region. The plane keeps out of trouble by moving too fast.

By the time it is travelling at 1000 miles an hour or more the swept-back wings are no longer needed to help the plane through the barrier. And, in fact, the normal straight wings are once again the most efficient design.

It is more than likely, therefore, that supersonic planes in future will be built with wings that can be moved in flight. Taking off with the normal straight-out wings, they will be swept back as the plane reaches towards the speed of sound, and then brought back to the original position when the barrier has been penetrated.

The experience of pilots who have flown at sonic speeds has shown that there are often difficulties in controlling the plane. In the region of the speed of sound the air pressure behind the compression wall is high, and the resistance offered to the plane is very great. Intense strains are thrown on the wings and fuselage—and yet the designer must cut down the thickness of his wing structures in order to avoid too great a pressure build-up. Spars used in the wing must be able to give it enormous strength at minimum thickness.

At supersonic speed planes have been known to slither and slide through the air, resisting control and even reversing the normal action of rudder and flaps. Most high-speed flying takes place at great heights, where the air is thin and there are few molecules to exert their pressure on the plane's control surfaces. At a height of 15 miles, for example, the air is exerting only a fortieth of its sea-level pressure. Although the plane needs less power to push it along at these heights, this tends to be achieved at the cost of diminished control. Bigger control surfaces must be used to make the most of the rarefied air. But as the planes fly higher still, the traditional techniques of control become virtually useless. At a height of 100 miles there is so little air that there would be nothing to press against a rudder or wing surface.

Planes flying at such heights, as they will undoubtedly do in the future, must use other methods of directional control.

Instead of depending on surface controls bearing against the air, they will, for example, use the thrust from rockets to guide them in the right direction. Jets of gas will take the place of flaps and rudders.

If these problems of high-speed flight were the only ones that the designer had to face they would make things difficult enough. But there are others that he cannot hope to solve until scientists have given him new metals and materials. Already, for example, flying speeds are reaching up into regions where friction-heat is having an appreciable effect on the structural strength of the plane.

At normal ground speeds the heat generated by friction between, say, a car or railway engine and the air through which it moves is so small that it need not be considered. At 60 miles an hour a car will have its body-work heated through something like one half of one degree Fahrenheit. But even before a plane is flying at near-sonic speeds, its temperature can rise by as much as twenty degrees.

To-day, with speeds reaching beyond a thousand miles an hour, friction-heat is becoming a really serious problem. At 1300 miles an hour, for example, the temperature rise through air friction can be as much as 200°F. This heating can have a variety of effects on the plane and pilot. Transparent plastic windows and canopies, which have become almost standard equipment on subsonic planes, will start to soften and lose their strength at 200°F. Insulation in electronic equipment of the plane may deteriorate, and radar aids break down. As temperatures rise the aluminium and magnesium alloys from which most planes are built will begin to lose their strength. Even at the comparatively low temperatures of 250°F.—not much hotter than boiling water—aluminium can lose more than a third of its strength. This means that aluminium airframe members must be made stronger and heavier in a plane that is going to travel at heat-generating speeds. Yet to attain these speeds the designer is constantly seeking ways of cutting down his plane's weight.

One answer to friction heat is to instal refrigeration equipment in the plane. But, again, this adds to the designer's dilemma—it means more weight and less useful space inside the plane. Nevertheless high-speed planes already carry cooling equipment to protect the pilot from being roasted inside his cockpit. As speeds increase the need for refrigeration equipment will extend to most parts of the plane as well.

Meanwhile every effort is being made to develop new structural materials that will retain their strength at comparatively high temperatures. The metal titanium, for example, is high on the list as an aircraft metal of the future. Titanium is as strong as steel, but only half its weight. Titanium alloys retain their strength at temperatures where aluminium has begun to weaken. Titanium therefore provides a combination of lightness, strength, and resistance to heat that is essential in modern plane construction.

There is ample titanium in the earth's crust. It is the seventh most common metal of all. But it is extremely difficult to extract economically from its ores.

Once titanium becomes available cheaply and in quantity it will find a tremendous future waiting for it in the air. So difficult has the problem of constructional strength at high temperatures become that modern high-speed planes are relying more and more on stainless steel to provide strength where heat is being generated. Stainless steel is heavy, but it retains the strength that is needed when it becomes hot.

With the materials now available, the 'heat barrier' will probably be reached at between 2600 and 2800 miles an hour. At this sort of speed the equipment needed to cool the plane will be so large and complex that it will be absorbing most of the power generated by the plane.

Temperature changes in the atmosphere are introducing other difficulties under modern flying conditions. Planes are flying in the stratosphere at heights of 40,000 feet or more. Here, above the weather, the pilot can get away from the clouds and storms that plague him at lower levels. But he has to put up with arctic temperatures. The air eight miles above the earth is often at $-70°F$.

If the plane flew fast enough the friction heat could be used to keep it warm. But at speeds of up to 500 miles an hour, such as we use in normal flying, the heat is inadequate to overcome the effects of the cold air. The surface of a plane flying through the stratosphere is often cooled twenty or thirty degrees below freezing point.

Constructional metals, plastics, hydraulic fluids, and other materials must be able to cope with such low temperatures, and the designer must also allow for actual shrinkage in the plane. Taking off from a tropical airfield and climbing to the stratosphere, a large airliner may well shrink by as much as six inches in its length.

Another hazard of stratosphere flight lies in the small amount of water vapour in the air. With only a thousandth of the water that there is at ground level, the thin high-level air can play unexpected tricks on aircraft engines and equipment. The carbon brushes in an aircraft's electric power plant will last for months at low levels; they will wear away in an hour or two in the desiccated stratosphere.

Although there are so many mechanical and structural problems to overcome as we fly faster and faster, and higher and higher in the air, the practical limits are now set by human factors. We can make a plane that will fly faster than sound, and survive. But the human body is finding that such speeds are subjecting it to more than it can bear without special precautions and protection.

Speed itself is not the problem. What matters is the change of speed—acceleration or deceleration. We can travel in a plane as comfortably at 1000 miles an hour as we can at 100 miles an hour as long as we do not make sudden changes in the speed or direction of the plane. Our bodies find difficulty in coping with the forces that play on them as a result of such changes.

In a high-speed diving turn a fighter pilot will find the blood being drained from one part of his body and forced into another. His head, for example, will go short of blood, which is being pressed into his legs. The forces acting on the soft parts of his body will be dragging them violently out of shape. His internal organs are subjected to enormous forces. A sharp turn, even at a speed of 350 miles an hour, can force a pilot floorward at six times the force of gravity. His body is literally pushed into his boots.

Under such conditions the heart is trying to pump blood through the body against tremendous odds. The effect of the centrifugal force is to increase the apparent weight of the blood until it becomes as heavy as molten metal. If the strain continues the head becomes starved of blood and oxygen. The eyes suffer and the pilot can no longer see. Finally, as his brain is starved of oxygen, he loses consciousness altogether.

The average man begins to lose effective vision at an acceleration equal to four times that of gravity, and he suffers a blackout in a few seconds. But he can withstand a great deal more by changing his position in such a way as to take some of the strain from his heart. Lying down, for example, a pilot can withstand ten times the force of gravity for two or three minutes at a time. Super-fast planes that have to be able to dive and turn rapidly in combat are being built to accommodate the pilot in a lying-down position.

Special suits have been devised to help the pilot to withstand acceleration. These suits fit closely to the body and carry inflatable bladders, which can be blown up to press against the thighs and other vulnerable parts. When the plane is subjecting the pilot to high acceleration compressed air from the engine inflates the bladders and helps the body to resist the weight which forces it out of its normal shape. With the help of modern suits of this type a pilot can withstand seven times the force of gravity.

In civilian flying the problems of living and breathing in the thin air of the stratosphere are being met by designing the plane so that it can carry its own atmosphere aloft. Cabins are pressurized, and the air inside is maintained at a pressure equivalent to that of the atmosphere at about 8000 feet. Passengers and crew can travel in comfort even though the air outside is too thin to support life. But there is always the chance that damage to the plane—a broken window or door—may allow the air to escape until the pressure inside the plane is as low as that outside. In military planes, which are liable to be damaged by bullet or shell-fire, this is an ever-present threat.

The effects of a sudden decompression of this sort can be varied and extremely dangerous. At 40,000 feet, for example, the air is at a fifth of the pressure it exerts at ground-level. The plane is flying in a partial vacuum, and if it is damaged the air rushes out until the air inside is at the same low pressure as that outside. In a

matter of a few seconds the occupants of the plane may
find themselves in an atmosphere containing only a fifth
of the air they are used to.

Although the air rushing from the damaged plane can
soon balance up the pressures inside and outside, the
air and gases inside the body cannot so easily do the
same. Normally these gases are at the same pressure as
the air outside. But as the outside pressure drops suddenly to a fraction of the normal, the gases inside the
body expand. Under severe decompression the body
will actually explode.

Moreover, as the outside pressure falls, nitrogen dissolved in the blood begins to escape in the form of
bubbles. This causes the painful condition called ' the
bends ', which afflicts deep-sea divers who have risen
too quickly from the high pressures on the sea bed.
' The bends ' can cause paralysis and death.

Again, a special suit can give individual protection
against these effects of decompression. Fitting close,
and carrying inflatable tubes to counter the fall in pressure, it keeps the body in more suitable pressure surroundings. A plastic helmet fits over the head and is
supplied with oxygen under pressure.

Even though these suits provide only temporary
relief, they can give a fighter pilot an extra fifteen
seconds of consciousness—enough to enable him to dive
down into more substantial air.

On top of these physical effects of decompression
there is the lack of oxygen itself. At heights of 40,000–
50,000 feet there is so little oxygen that it is insufficient
to support life. An unprotected flier suffocates, even
when extra oxygen is supplied to him through a normal
breathing tube. The low atmospheric pressure is insufficient to allow the blood to absorb the necessary amount
of oxygen. At 35,000 feet lack of oxygen can cause un-
consciousness in half a minute. At 50,000 feet, even with

extra oxygen being supplied, a pilot will survive for only
ten seconds.

Oxygen shortage is one of the most important aspects
of high-altitude flight. Its effects begin to be felt at comparatively low levels. As low as 7000 feet vision can
be impaired through lack of oxygen in the blood reaching the sensory receptor cells of the retina. As the brain
itself becomes starved of oxygen it is unable to sustain
the pilot's proper judgment. His intelligence is impaired
without his realizing that anything is wrong; he does
not appreciate the need for taking immediate action to
put things right.

Portable electro - encephalographs — brain - wave
machines—have been used as warning devices to guard
against the effects of oxygen starvation. As soon as the
lack of oxygen begins to affect the pilot's proper thought
routines the pattern of the brain waves changes and the
machine rings a warning bell.

As planes fly faster and higher the demands on the
pilots are increasing. A modern fighter plane may
have a hundred controls to operate, with forty instruments and warning lights to watch. Yet the faster he
flies, the less time the pilot or navigator has in which to
act.

In the stratosphere the pilot finds that his normal
vision background is reversed. Below him are the brilliant white clouds reflecting the sunshine. Above there
is only the thin upper atmosphere between him and the
limitless voids of space. Without the myriad particles
to split and reflect the sunlight the sky is no longer blue
and bright. It is as dark as night, with the sun glaring
brilliantly like a massive searchlight.

Within the plane the shadows thrown by the intense
sunlight are sharp and deep. Instruments are difficult
to read. With only a thin blanket of air to filter out the
harmful ultra-violet rays the sunlight itself is fierce and

dangerous. Its glare is ten times as great as it is on the ground below.

As we leave the protection of our blanket, the air, even the cosmic rays become dangerous. Eight miles high the intensity of cosmic rays is a hundred times as great as at ground level. This is approaching danger-point, where the radiations could become a real hazard to passengers and crew.

So, as we reach higher and faster into the skies, the problems and difficulties are increasing and multiplying. We have reached a stage in flying where a host of human and technical problems have built up into a formidable barrier. Undoubtedly this barrier will be broken down in time, and we shall enter a new era of flight, as exciting as that which the Wright brothers began more than half a century ago.

4

A Surfeit of Sound

THE moving air, by bringing us the weather, can influence our lives in many ways. But air in movement has another, quite different, part to play in the organization of life on earth. Air is the medium that carries sound and so makes possible our sense of hearing.

The sounds we hear are caused by movements in the drum of tissue that closes up each ear. Vibrations of these eardrums are passed on, through delicate and complex mechanisms, until they reach the inner ear. Here the physical movements are translated into nervous impulses; these impulses are despatched to the brain, which is informed that the eardrum has vibrated through a certain pattern of movement.

The vibrations of the eardrum which give us, in this way, our sense of hearing are caused in their turn by vibrations in the air. Anything that is moving in the air will make the little particles of atmospheric gas move too, and each particle will pass its movement to neighbouring particles. In this way the disturbance is transmitted through the air; the effect is like the ripple of movement that passes down a stationary train as the engine jerks forward.

If the movement of the particles of air is caused by something that vibrates rhythmically backwards and forwards the particles will move in sympathy to and fro. This vibration of the particles of air will spread out in all directions from its source; as it reaches the air in

contact with the human ear it passes on its movement
to the eardrum and we ' hear ' the vibrations as a recog-
nizable sound.

Normally the air is alive with a multitude of different
vibrations coming from innumerable sources of sound.
The air of an office will be filled with movement carrying the sounds of the traffic in the street outside, the
noise of typewriters and the ringing of bells, the scrape
of chairs and feet and the hum of human voices. Each
source is sending out its own vibrations, which speed
out through the air and induce a complex system of
vibrations in the eardrum that detects them. Yet the
sense of hearing is so wonderfully designed that sounds
can all be sorted and identified by the brain.

Although the sounds we hear are infinitely varied in
their character, they all transmit their vibrations
through the air at the same speed. Sound travels through
the air at sea-level at about a fifth of a mile a second.
The crack of a rifle reaches us no faster than the tinkle
of a cycle bell. The speed of sound is unaffected by the
atmospheric pressure, but it is influenced by changes in
the temperature; the warmer the air, the faster will
sound travel through it. Planes can fly faster in tropical
regions before being troubled by compression built up
at the speed of sound.

Sound waves are characterized by the number of to-
and-fro movements they make a second, and also by the
distance through which the movement takes place. The
number of vibrations a second is called the frequency,
and the extent of the movement is the amplitude.

Frequency determines the pitch of the note we hear.
An eardrum vibrating 2000 times a second is registering
a note lower than one vibrating 10,000 times a second.
The amplitude, on the other hand, determines the intensity of the sound. The greater the to-and-fro movement,
the louder is the sound registered by the brain.

In ordinary circumstances most of the sounds we hear are composite vibrations, made up from many different frequencies and amplitudes. Variations in these characteristics provide us with the myriads of different sounds that make the sense of hearing such a rich and rewarding one.

As sound vibrations radiate through the air the amplitude becomes smaller. But the frequency remains the same. The loudness with which we hear a sound is therefore lessened by distance, but the pitch is the same no matter how far we are from the source.

In musical instruments sound vibrations are created in many different ways. Tight-stretched strings vibrate as they are struck by the hammers in a piano, inducing similar vibrations in the particles of air beside them. In the guitar and the harp strings are pulled aside and then released; in the violin or cello they are stroked with a bow, which causes vibrations by continually catching up the strings and releasing them. In a xylophone sound is produced by vibrations of solid bars as they are struck; each bar vibrates with a frequency that is characteristic of its shape and size. In a drum it is a sheet of stretched parchment that vibrates; in the organ the column of air itself is given rhythmic movement inside a pipe.

Human beings create the sounds they use in speech by making air vibrate as it comes from the respiratory system. Other vertebrates use respiratory air in this way, but the sounds are limited and the technique less refined.

Of the invertebrate animals only the arthropods, with their hard, jointed body coverings, have genuine sound-producing devices. Grasshoppers and crickets make sections of their body vibrate by rubbing them together. Cicadas create an impressive noise by vibrating special discs that are built into their bodies.

Many animal sounds, but not all, can be heard by

human beings. The range of hearing differs greatly from one species to another. Human hearing is restricted to sound vibrations in the range of frequencies between about 20 and 20,000 per second. The range diminishes with age; middle-aged people are often deaf to frequencies above 10,000 and cannot hear everyday sounds in the higher register, like the songs of birds or the noise of hissing steam.

Dogs can hear sounds an octave higher than can human beings. 'Noiseless' dog whistles send out vibrations at frequencies above 20,000 per second; the dog can hear the sounds, but the owner cannot.

Canaries are deaf below high C, but can hear sounds too shrill for human beings to detect. Rats can squeak two octaves too high for us to hear them. Frogs, on the other hand, are bass and contralto; their range of hearing extends to only 10,000 vibrations a second.

The human ear has developed into an intricate apparatus that can discriminate between all sorts of different vibrations within its range. Its sensitivity is at its highest in the region of 1000–5000 vibrations a second. Other animals have hearing systems which are much less delicate and complex; they are adequate for picking up sounds but are not called upon to translate these sounds into the words and sentences of language.

Some insects 'hear' through sensitive hairs that detect vibrations in the air. In soft-skinned animals the sense of hearing is also closely linked with the sense of touch; vibrations are detected by the skin. Fish can respond to sounds and will distinguish pitch variations equal to intervals of a minor third in the middle range of the piano.

The finely balanced mechanism of the human ear enables us to use our sense of hearing as part of our communication system. But it has its disadvantages as well; it leaves us open to a continuous assault by sound waves, whether we want to hear them or not. We have to put up with noise.

Our modern air has become filled with a bewildering variety of sounds. Cars and lorries roar and rattle along the roads; jet planes are screaming overhead in numbers that increase from day to day; even at home mechanized lawn mowers and vacuum cleaners, electric polishers and food mixers are adding steadily to the sounds that batter against our eardrums.

This ordeal by sound is more than just an irritation that must be accepted as a part of modern living conditions; it is becoming a serious threat to economic efficiency and personal health.

The effect of the impact of sound upon our senses depends upon the strength, or loudness, of the vibrations in the air. Instruments have been devised to measure loudness, and sounds can be defined in units of decibels. The threshold of human hearing, where we just begin to hear a sound, is equal to a loudness of zero decibels. The other end of the decibel scale, where the strength of sound becomes intolerable and vibrations cause physical damage and pain, corresponds to a sound intensity of 130–135 decibels. Most ordinary sounds fall within the range between these two extremes.

The gentle noises of a garden, with the wind rustling the leaves of the trees, will reach a sound intensity of 10 to 20 decibels. A low whisper is in the region of 20 decibels. Even in the quiet of the countryside we cannot escape entirely from sounds. The distant noise of trains and traffic, the mooing of a cow, and the stir of the wind will fill the air with 20 decibels of sound, though the silence appears complete by contrast with the noises of a town.

These sounds, and the sounds of normal home life, are accepted by human beings without dismay. Up to a noise value of about 50 decibels we do not feel disturbed

by the loudness of the sounds that reach our ears. But
above this loudness level sounds begin to worry us.
Subconsciously our bodies are resisting the persistent
onslaught of vibrations in our ears. At 70–80 decibels
noise has reached a stage where it is damaging and
dangerous if we have to suffer it for long.

Nowadays we live and work in surroundings where
the air is often filled with noise that is too loud. A busy
street can reach as high as 70 decibels, and an underground train 85. A squad of clacking typists will raise
the noise level of an office to 70 or 80 decibels; a pneumatic drill in the road outside the window can send out
90 decibels or more.

One of the difficulties in studying the effect of noise
on human beings comes from the differences in our
personal reactions to noise. Strictly speaking, the level
of noise-intensity measured by instruments in decibels
is not the same as loudness. One person will find noise
of a certain decibel level a good deal ' louder ' than another person hearing the same sound. Loudness depends
on individual reaction, whereas decibels give a scientific
measure of the strength of the noise. To establish its
personal effects more accurately noise has been treated
on a basis of loudness. The unit of loudness is the phon.
But for most practical purposes the decibel provides a
reasonable unit of noise on which to work.

Another problem in dealing with the effects of noise
lies in the peculiar psychological differences in our
reactions to it. A dripping tap at night, for example,
can drive us into a frenzy. Yet the gentle fall of rain
from a tree after a storm can lull us into contented sleep.
The intensity of the noise in each case, measured in
decibels, may be identical. In the same way the sound
of a neighbour's wireless can set our teeth on edge; yet
we can enjoy the same programme from our own radio,
reaching us at the same decibel value. Sounds are so

bound up with personal experiences and prejudices that their effects cannot be judged entirely on a decibel figure.

It does not need a scientist to tell us that loud noises can be disastrous to our peace of mind. Working in an atmosphere of continuous noise can make us irritable and jumpy. Even modest levels of noise have a serious influence on health and efficiency.

At the top of the decibel scale noise can be loud enough to do real physical and mental damage; it will cause neurosis and nausea. The loudest man-made noise of all—the scream and screech from the engines of a jet plane—can reach 140 decibels. This super-noise will break down the tissue in a human being. Small animals, like rats and mice, have been killed by noise of this intensity; cockroaches, mosquitoes, and other insects will die in a few seconds.

Some occupations are notorious for their noise. Boiler-makers and riveters work in surroundings that are vibrant with the clang and crash of metal. As long ago as 1886 scientists found that boilermakers—almost to a man—were suffering from a permanent and progressive deafness caused by the noise that beat against their ear-drums. In some factories, where noise is at its worst, defective hearing is a qualification for the job. Deafness protects the workers against the effects of their noisy occupations.

The noise of jet planes has brought entirely new problems for the sound scientist. Airports are already among the noisiest places in the world; they are becoming steadily worse as more and more jet planes take the air.

A modern four-engined piston aircraft creates a noise-irritation area three miles wide and thirteen miles long during take-off. But the area of noise-irritation covered during the take-off of a six-engined jet transport plane is four miles wide and twenty-four miles long; with a four-engined turboprop plane it extends to thirty-two miles.

Jet-plane noises have little effect on the pilot of the plane, who is sitting well forward of the jets that are creating their intense vibrations. The problem of protection against the 120–140 decibel noise relates particularly to the service crew and airfield personnel, and to people living in the neighbourhood of a busy airfield.

Guinea-pigs exposed to the noises of jet engines have been burned to death by the heat generated in their vibrating bodies. Men who have submitted themselves to the effect of jet-engine noise have suffered temporary deafness and local skin heating. The strength has gone from their muscles, and their vision has been impaired.

The effects of these loud noises at the upper end of the decibel scale becomes self-evident after comparatively short exposure times. But more and more people are having to spend much of their time in surroundings where the level of sound is in the 50–100 decibel region. The effect of this sort of noise, common enough in modern offices and workshops, in the street, and even in the house, is not so easy to assess. The loudness of the noise is above the level at which irritation begins but below that at which immediate and obvious damage may be caused. A great deal of research is being carried out to determine the effects of this sort of 'moderate' noise on human health and efficiency.

In an atmosphere of noise above the level of 50–60 decibels the human body is working under constant strain. The assault upon the eardrums creates a sense of tension; nerves become frayed and irritability increases. The pulse-rate is affected, and blood pressure rises. This strain of living and working in noisy surroundings prevents the body relaxing, and the end of the day is reached in a state of great fatigue. At night noise can prevent us getting a restful sleep even though we do not consciously hear it. Our eyes are forced to rest when they are covered by the eyelids; but there is nothing to stop vibrations entering our ears when we are sleeping.

The fatigue that is caused by noise cuts down our working efficiency. Tests have shown that we often use a fifth more energy to do a job in noisy surroundings than we would use under peaceful conditions. Noise affects our judgment and power of concentration; part of the brain is occupying itself with sounds that it does not really want to hear.

These physical and mental effects are reflected in the efficiency with which we carry out our jobs. By cutting down the noise in one factory from 100 to 75 decibels, sound engineers reduced the accident rate by nearly half and stepped up output by a fifth. Noise abatement in a motor works brought down the consumption of headache pills by half. By putting a new bearing on a noisy ventilator a factory manager raised the output from his works by 12 per cent.

A large United States insurance company got remarkable results by reducing office noises. A drop of eight decibels in the noise level cut down typists' errors by almost a third and those of machine operators by a half. Health was improved and absenteeism reduced. The staff were more contented, and job-changing was cut by 47 per cent. The company estimated that, by this simple policy of noise abatement, it increased overall efficiency by 9 per cent. and saved fifty-eight dollars per employee during the first year.

A survey of some 5000 offices showed that in more than half of them noise was interfering with efficiency. Where efforts were made to reduce noise, efficiency and accuracy were consistently improved. The effects were most easily assessed in the case of routine workers, but were even greater in the case of executives, who were better able to concentrate on their jobs.

Too much noise can affect the eyesight as well as increasing nervous strain. The relation between hearing and sight is quite pronounced. In order to hear faint noises, we screw our eyes up; after hearing loud noises we need more light to see by. Noisy motorcars are more dangerous to drive than silent ones.

The effects of noise are felt throughout the range of audible vibrations, from 20 to 20,000 a second. But pitch, or frequency, plays a large part in determining the amount of damage done. The human ear can put up with a barrage of loud, low-pitched noises better than it can withstand shriller noises of lower intensity. Noise has its greatest effect at a frequency of about 4000 vibrations per second. French scientists have confirmed what many parents already knew; the scratching of a violin E string is one of the most irritating of all the noises we are called upon to bear.

Sound vibrations in the region of 20,000 a second are about as shrill as human ears can hear. This top limit of the human range is the sort of noise we get from jingling keys. But in the mysterious world of silent sound, where frequencies are too high for us to hear, the waves can be vibrating millions of times a second. These ultrasonic waves have become the subject of a great deal of research.

Special techniques have been devised for generating high-frequency ultrasonic waves. One of the most effective methods makes use of crystals which can change their shape under the influence of electricity. When a crystal of quartz, for example, is given an electric shock, it expands or shrinks depending on the way the current is trying to flow. If we subject a crystal of this sort to a rapidly alternating current of electricity it will expand and contract at high speed. By clamping one side of the crystal firmly we can make the other side vibrate in and out like the parchment of a drum. And if it is vibrating fast enough the crystal surface will compress and expand the air beside it to produce ultrasonic waves.

Another way of doing the job is by using the change in length of a metal rod when it is magnetized. A piece of iron, for example, can be given doses of magnetization which follow one another rapidly. This makes the iron bar expand and contract at high speed, producing ultrasonic waves in the air alongside it.

Modern ultrasonic generators can create vibrations of up to fifty million times a second—a note more than 2000 times as shrill as the human ear can detect. The distance over which each vibration takes place may be as small as one twenty-five thousandth part of an inch. But the energy delivered is of terrific intensity. Cotton wool held in a beam of ultrasonic waves will catch fire. Heat is generated by the friction resulting from vibrations 50,000 times as intense as those from a thunder clap.

Portable ultrasonic generators have been developed in which the vibrating mechanism is in a box small enough to go into the pocket. The box is connected by a flexible tube to an electrical generator which provides the alternating current that produces the vibrations. Put into a tank of water, a generator of this sort will churn the surface of the water violently and send a steaming fountain into the air.

Ultrasonic waves are used in industry for testing metal castings. A beam of waves fired into the casting will be reflected from the surface of a crack or flaw. By measuring the time taken for the echo to return the tester can tell if there are flaws in the metal. This echo principle is used for detecting submarines. Ultrasonic vibrations sent out from a ship are reflected back by the submarine. The time taken for the echo to return gives a measure of the distance that the submarine is from the ship. In peacetime the same principle is used for estimating ocean depths, locating wrecks, and detecting shoals of fish.

Ultrasonic waves can kill germs: the vibrations literally shake bacteria to pieces. Ultrasonic waves have been used for sterilizing milk without heating it. Ordinary pasteurization is apt to affect the flavour of milk; ultrasonic sterilization does not. By using this technique milk can be sterilized during transit in road or rail tankers. An ultrasonic generator drawing its power from the wheels will disintegrate the germs whilst the milk is on its way to the dairy.

As well as killing bacteria in milk, ultrasonic waves break up the tiny globules of fat into finer particles. The milk becomes more uniform in texture, and the cream does not settle out. The milk is uniformly creamy, keeps longer, and is easily digested.

Industry is using ultrasonic waves to mix awkward liquids. Molten metals are often difficult to mix when one is very much heavier than the other; ultrasonic waves will shake up molten metals such as iron and lead into a uniform mixture. Even mercury and water will turn into a grey, milky liquid that does not settle out for several hours.

Chocolate manufacturers have found that they can cut down mixing times by using ultrasonic waves. A process taking seventy-five hours to make a really smooth paste can be done in twenty-five minutes with high frequency vibrations helping out.

In the home ultrasonic waves could give us germ-free larders more efficient than a ' fridge.' Ultrasonic bursts would destroy decay germs in the air. Ultrasonic waves can do an excellent job of laundering on the dirtiest clothes, and ultrasonic washing machines are in use.

High frequency sound waves are generated in the water. In a matter of minutes the vibrations have taken the dirt from the clothes. There is no harsh abrasion or knocking about to harm the fabrics.

One of the difficulties of bringing ultrasonics into widespread use is their possible effect on the human body. Ultrasonic waves will shake living cells to pieces as effectively as they will destroy bacteria. Blood corpuscles are disrupted, and a dose of ultrasonics can bring on high temperature and symptoms of fever. Research scientists working with the waves have suffered from nausea and headaches and have lost their sense of balance.

With jet planes as a source of ultrasonic shrieking on a large scale research is now being carried out to assess the effects these ' silent noises ' may have on the human body. Scientists are at the same time studying ultrasonic waves for medical use. There are indications, for example, that they may be of value against cancer. They have been used for rheumatism and sciatica; the waves appear to function as a source of heat. Ultrasonic waves have been used against animal and insect pests. Rats and mice cannot stand bombardment with the waves and can be cleared from an infested house. Insects have been blown to pieces in a field of crops.

This ability of ultrasonic waves to destroy life has not been overlooked by military experts. An ultrasonic ' death-ray ' has been considered as a possible weapon. Such rays have killed fish and frogs, and small animals like mice.

Ultrasonic vibrations can remove the particles of dirt and dust from factory smoke. The filth poured out on us from factory chimneys often consists of valuable by-products that the factories would prefer to keep if they could. But particles of solid or liquid matter in industrial smokes are sometimes extremely small and difficult to precipitate. When ultrasonic waves are fired into the smoke the particles are made to vibrate backwards and forwards. The distance they move may be only a thousandth of an inch. But the push they get from the waves is a powerful one, and any particles that collide with each other tend to stick. As larger particles do not move so readily as the smaller ones, the small particles are flung against the larger ones. In this way the ultrasonic vibrations make the fine smoke particles collect together a hundred or so at a time until they reach a size where they are large enough to settle.

Ultrasonic installations of this type have been able to recover more than 96 per cent. of the carbon particles in industrial smoke—a by-product that is well worth having. Acid vapours and tar fogs have been dealt with in the same way.

Ultrasonic waves have been tested against natural fogs. The moisture particles in fog are small enough to float in the air. If they could be built up into larger particles they would fall to the ground. In one experiment with ultrasonic waves, twelve huge ultrasonic sirens cleared fog from an airfield runway. But the waves brought stunned birds falling to the ground as well and affected airfield personnel.

The influence of ultrasonic waves may reach to atoms and molecules. Whisky treated with high-frequency waves has matured in two years instead of four, and beer is sweetened and improved in flavour. These effects are probably due to chemical changes stimulated by ultrasonic vibrations.

During World War I echo-sounding instruments came into their own for detecting U-boats; since then their devices have been adopted widely as navigational aids. Yet it was only during World War II that scientists discovered how Nature had perfected an identical system for use by animals. Bats, for example, carry their own ultrasonic echo-location equipment to help them as they fly.

Biologists have long suspected that bats possess a sixth sense which enables them to fly in darkness without colliding with obstacles in their way. Bats can fly, hundreds together, through narrow twisting caves without a glimmer of light to help them. They can flit among trees and telephone wires at night. During the eighteenth century Swiss and Italian scientists proved that bats could fly between obstacles even when their eyes were covered. But when their ears were covered, the bats could not avoid the obstacles in their way. Somehow the bats were using sound to help them to 'see' objects ahead of them. Yet the animals made only the faintest of squeals as they flew.

The nature of the bat's sixth sense remained a mystery until 1920 when a British scientist suggested that bats were using inaudible ultrasonic waves to warn them of obstacles. These waves sent out through the air would be reflected from anything in the way; the bat would be able to detect the echo. The time taken for the echo of the ultrasonic squeals to return would give the bat a measure of its distance from the obstacle.

For nearly twenty years this theory remained unchecked. During World War II American scientists began a study of the bat's location system. And with the help of ultrasonic detectors they confirmed that the animals were indeed emitting ultrasonic waves.

Wires were stretched from floor to ceiling in rooms where bats were allowed to fly. The scientists found that the bats could navigate between these wires quite confidently, even when their eyes were covered. But if either the mouth or the ears were covered the bats collided with the wires in their path. Even with one ear covered the bats lost their ability to locate the obstacles. They could presumably estimate their distance from the obstacle with only one ear receiving echoes; but, like human beings, they needed both ears to give them the precise direction from which the echo was returning.

With the help of sensitive detectors the scientists found that the bats were emitting waves in the region of 50,000–100,000 vibrations a second at tremendous intensity. The loudness of the ultrasonic shriek is in the region of 113 decibels—about the same as the noise of a pneumatic road drill at its worst.

Bats send out their ultrasonic waves in bursts, adjusting the number of bursts to suit their requirements. At rest the bat contents himself with ten ultrasonic cries a second. When he is flying, and there are no obstacles in his path, he sends out twenty to thirty bursts a second. But as soon as danger threatens, and he detects something in the way, the bat increases his bursts of waves to fifty or sixty a second.

Detailed study of the bat's ultrasonic cries has shown that each ultrasonic burst lasts little more than 1/500 of a second and contains about 100 vibrations. Further experiments have shown that the bat has adapted its location system in a remarkable way to enable it to detect objects only a few inches ahead of it.

At such short distances the echo from an obstacle will return before the bat has completed his ultrasonic burst. The bat has had to make arrangements, therefore, to modify the echo in such a way that it does not get mixed up with the squeak.

Careful studies of the bat's cries have shown how this is done. The animal uses a 'frequency modulation' system similar to that being introduced in modern F.M. radio. When the bat sends out its ultrasonic burst it begins on a frequency of some 100,000 vibrations a second. As the cry proceeds the frequency falls steadily until it is only about 50,000 at the tail end of the cry.

When the echo of the early part of the cry returns from an object a few inches away it is at a pitch corresponding to a frequency of 100,000 a second. But by this time the bat is sending out a 'lower note' of perhaps 60,000 vibrations a second. It can therefore distinguish between the echo and the last part of its cry.

As bats often live together in colonies, they have had to add another refinement to their location system. Each bat has an individual combination of frequencies in its ultrasonic burst, enabling it to recognize the echo of its own voice in air that is throbbing with vibrations like a silent Tower of Babel.

5

The Wonderful Weather

THE air in the lower levels of our atmosphere is rarely still. As it moves over the surface of the earth it brings all the infinite variations of warmth and cold, rain and snow, cloud and fog, that created the conditions in our environment that we call the weather.

Weather is something that affects us all in our daily lives. Men have been studying the vagaries of the weather for hundreds of years, trying to assess the relationship between causes and effects. Over 2000 years ago the Greeks were recording wind directions. They gave us the word Meteorology, meaning 'the study of the things above.' Aristotle and his follower Theophrastus wrote essays about winds and rain. But any real study was impossible without instruments to measure the various factors involved in atmospheric changes. The philosophers were waiting for someone to invent the barometer and other gadgets that could be used to measure different properties of the air at any time.

The Italian scientist Torricelli, a pupil of Galileo, made the first barometer in 1643. It was a long glass tube containing a column of liquid held up by the pressure of the air. The height of the column depended upon the pressure of the atmosphere immediately above it. By measuring the length of the liquid column it was possible to get an accurate record of atmospheric pressure.

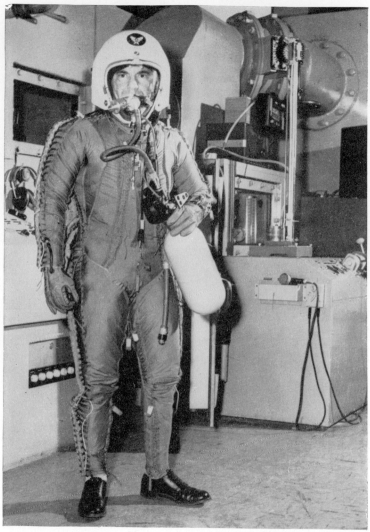

Photo U. S. Air Force

MC-4 HIGH ALTITUDE PRESSURE SUIT.

The pilot wore this suit when he reached 198,770 feet in an altitude chamber test.

WEATHER RESEARCH
IN THE UPPER
ATMOSPHERE

The robot passenger carried by a weather balloon consists of a radio transmitter and three weather-measuring instruments. When the balloon bursts, high in the air, the equipment is parachuted back to earth.

A weather balloon is sent up from the *Weather Watcher* in the Atlantic. By following its course, with the help of radar, observers will note wind-direction in the upper air.

Some four years earlier another Italian, Benedetto Castelli, devised a rain-gauge. The thermometer was being brought into general use at this time by the Grand Duke Ferdinand II, of Tuscany, who became sufficiently interested in meteorology to set up a number of weather recording stations. He used their observations for what must have been the first of all the forecasts based on scientific facts.

During the seventeenth and eighteenth centuries meteorology was caught up in the scientific renaissance. Accurate observation and measurement began to provide a background to the study of atmospheric change as a whole. Scientists interested themselves in what was going on in the upper air as well as at sea level.

By 1752 Benjamin Franklin was sending up his kites into thunderstorms to see what happened. A few years later the French scientist Charles made a balloon ascent of one and a half miles into the upper air over Paris. In 1804 Gay-Lussac reached a height of nearly four miles.

During the early nineteenth century a mass of information accumulated about the weather. But it was not until scientists could study huge regions of the atmosphere as a whole that any understanding could come from the information that was available. The weather in any particular locality at any time is an insignificant part of atmospheric changes operating over vast areas of the earth's surface. Before he can understand his weather the meteorologist needs information from many observers stationed at points scattered over as wide an area as possible. Moreover he must be able to arrange for all the observations to be taken at exactly the same time.

The first real attempt to study weather in this way was made by a German meteorologist called Brandes in 1820. Brandes plotted the first synoptic charts—charts showing measurements of pressure, temperature, and other factors taken at the same time over different parts of the earth's surface. But the study of weather over a country or continent in those days was almost impossible owing to the slowness of communications.

The discovery of the electric telegraph in 1837 was the answer to the meteorologist's prayer. In 1848 a paper was read at a Swansea meeting of the British Association outlining the value of the telegraph in weather study. Since then telegraphic communication and meteorology have grown up side by side.

The founding of the British Meteorological Society in 1850 provided the co-ordination that was needed in meteorology. One of the most advanced of all the weather scientists at that time was Admiral Robert Fitzroy, Chief of the Meteorological Department of the Board of Trade. In 1860 Fitzroy began collecting weather reports by telegraph. A year later he sent out gale warnings to shipping and made daily forecasts of the weather. Fitzroy made a study of the relationship between his barometric readings and the weather that they presaged. He worked out a series of simple forecasting 'rules' that are still in general use to-day. Fitzroy first told us, for example, that a gradual rise in the barometer means settled weather, whereas a rapid fall is warning of a storm.

In 1867 the Meteorological Department was taken over by the Royal Society and forecasts were abandoned. But public demand brought them back, and we have had them ever since. In 1875 *The Times* published the first weather maps to appear in a daily newspaper.

Official recognition and encouragement of the importance of meteorology gave a great stimulus to its development. The number of recording stations increased steadily, and the air over Victorian England was darkened by balloons carrying scientists ever higher into the atmosphere. On September 5, 1862, Mr James Glaisher, Secretary of the British Meteorological Society, took his barometer to a height of seven miles in an open balloon.

Manned balloons, however, were restricted in their use. In 1927 French meteorologists introduced the radio-sonde balloon which has become a vital part of meteorological equipment to-day. The radio-sonde is a small hydrogen-filled balloon carrying meteorological equipment that radios its information to the ground as it ascends. In 1937 the British meteorological station at Larkhill began using similar unmanned balloons to measure wind in the upper air by using radar to follow the balloon.

On August 30, 1848, weather information was first telegraphed to London by twenty-nine towns. Twenty-eight of them had sunshine; Manchester was the exception. To-day the Central Forecasting Office at Dunstable is in touch with weather stations all over the world. Britain alone has over 150 meteorological stations, and there are at least 5000 in Europe.

As weather information arrives at the Central Forecasting Office it is collated and retransmitted to all the reporting stations. Each station is kept continually in touch with the world's weather and can base its local forecast on general atmospheric conditions.

At five minutes to every hour the weather stations send in their weather information to Dunstable. By ten minutes past they are receiving the collective bulletin back again.

In the forecast room at Dunstable weather information coming in from all over the Northern Hemisphere is analysed and charted as it arrives. Charts covering Europe and the North Atlantic are prepared eight times a day. Smaller scale charts of weather in the Northern

Hemisphere and charts showing conditions in the upper air are made up four times a day.

In the forecast room the weather experts can watch the way conditions in the atmosphere are changing over half the surface of the world. They can build up the knowledge and experience that enable them to predict what to-morrow's weather will be like. Much of the information sent in from modern meteorological stations is obtained by radio-sonde balloons. From stations in Britain and overseas stations under British control these balloons are sent up several times a day.

As the hydrogen-filled balloons ascend they carry with them a compact meteorological outfit which radios information on pressure, temperature, and humidity of the air at different levels. Eventually the balloon bursts —often as high as twelve miles above the earth—and the instruments are brought back by parachute. Each outfit costs about £4, and every effort is made to retrieve the instruments. They have a special card attached, and anyone finding a radio-sonde outfit is asked to post the card immediately. This brings a box for packing the instruments and a reward of 5s. Of the 18,000 radio-sonde balloons used every year, some 4000 are recovered. Many losses are from balloons sent up by weather ships in the North Atlantic. Nine ships are maintained in this area under international control.

Like other sciences, meteorology is very much alive to the value of research. Instruments are constantly being improved, and techniques are developing rapidly. Mathematical interpretations of the masses of facts and figures are being studied to try and extend the range of accurate forecasting.

One difficulty in statistical work of this sort lies in the tedious mathematical drudgery that is often involved. Calculations that could help us predict next week's weather may take six months to work out. But the development of modern computing machines is helping us over this difficulty. Computers can do their sums in a matter of minutes where the mathematician would take months.

Computers are being used to provide experimental weather forecasts a month or six weeks ahead. Such forecasts are of limited value; our present difficulties in long-range forecasting derive not only from mathematics but from an insufficient understanding of weather science as a whole.

The meteorological service in Britain costs about two million pounds a year. There is no way of estimating the value of the service in terms of cash returns in agriculture, radio, the airlines, road and rail services, films, gas and electricity, fishing, the Forces, and all the other industries and activities to which a knowledge of to-morrow's weather means so much. But it is certainly very good value for money.

By comparison with the physicist or chemist, the meteorologist needs little in the way of equipment. His laboratory is the atmosphere and the materials of his one continuous experiment are air and water and heat. But the very size of his experimental territory makes life distressing for him. Things are happening throughout the atmosphere which he must know about if he is to understand his science. This means that trained observers must be stationed at strategic points over the entire surface of the earth.

To-day we are better off in the way of weather stations than we have ever been before. But as the demands on meteorology increase more and more information is needed by the meteorologist. Conditions in the upper levels of the troposphere are becoming of supreme importance in long-range forecasting; the course of the jet stream, for example, has a major influence on the weather. Meteorological stations are making increasing use of radio-sonde balloons and radar to obtain information about the upper air.

During the last twenty years weather forecasting has made more progress than it did during the previous century. In the Second World War meteorology came into its own. Weather information was a major factor in the successful timing of every military operation, from a bombing raid to the landings on the coast of Normandy.

The mass of information obtained by weather stations all over the world has enabled meteorologists to establish a real understanding of their science. Accurate observation of the behaviour of the atmosphere is bringing together cause and effect. It is becoming possible to predict with increasing accuracy what the atmospheric conditions experienced now will lead to in the future.

Although the interpretation and detailed study of the state of the atmosphere are complex, the basic principles behind the changing weather are comparatively simple. They depend upon variations in the movement, warmth, and moisture content of the air.

Apart from local variations, the air always contains the same proportion of oxygen, nitrogen, carbon dioxide, and other gases. But the amount of water vapour varies from day to day and from place to place. Water vapour is the most important atmospheric constituent of all so far as the weather is concerned. The amount of water vapour in the air determines whether the air is able to absorb more water vapour or whether it wants to get rid of some of it as rain.

The weight of air depends on its temperature—the hotter it is, the less it weighs. A column of hot air presses down less on the surface of the earth than a column of cold air of the same height. Also, water vapour is lighter than air, so that air containing a lot of water vapour tends to be lighter than dry air. When the barometer is 'low' it often means that the air has plenty of water in it—water that can appear as rain.

The equipment needed to record meteorological conditions is not complex. A thermometer gives the air temperature; an anemometer will measure wind speed, and a weather vane shows which way it is blowing; the rate at which water evaporates from a wet and dry bulb thermometer provides a measure of the moisture in the air, and the barometer gives the air pressure. These instruments will all provide facts in terms of figures; this information is supplemented by careful observation of weather conditions.

The amount of cloud, and its height and nature, will indicate what things are like in the upper atmosphere. The rate at which rain is falling can be measured by collecting water that falls in a definite area. The height of the level of this water in a standard vessel describes the rainfall as so many 'inches.'

Fog or mist, snow, frost, thunder, dew—any additional facts relating to the weather are meat and drink to the meteorologist and help him in his work. At stations all over the world trained observers record everything they can about the weather. Much of the information is in the form of figures given by meteorological instruments; the rest is a matter of accurate observation.

This is the information that is collected and reissued as a weather report by the Meteorological Office. The most important feature is the pressure map. By joining up points of equal pressure the meteorologist builds a 'contour' map showing where there are areas of high pressure—ridges, anticyclones, or 'highs'—and areas of low pressure like the depression that is rarely far away from Iceland. These areas of pressure differences cause winds; air flows from regions of high pressure to those where the pressure is low. Winds carry moisture and heat; they mean changes in atmospheric conditions of one sort or another. By developing an understanding of such factors it is possible to foresee what is going to happen when that ridge of high pressure starts moving towards the Faroes.

In spite of all the information that pours into the Meteorological Office daily, and on which reports are based, the meteorologist is groping in the dark in many ways. He is studying an experiment in an apparatus so large that he may know little of what is happening over thousands of square miles; and yet conditions can vary considerably over a matter of a mile or two. His observations tell him mostly what is going on at sea-level; he has limited knowledge of conditions in the atmosphere above, where things are happening that will be reflected in the weather below. Radio-sonde balloons carrying automatic recording equipment are finding out what is happening in the upper air, but to be of major value they must be used on an unprecedented scale.

The meteorologist is like a pianist being asked to play from music that gives him two or three notes on every line. He cannot guarantee the accuracy in detail until the information is all there.

It is this uncertainty in the best of weather forecasts that can make meteorology so intriguing as a hobby for the amateur. Every day the world conditions are presented to us by the Meteorological Office. This gives us a very broad picture as a starting-point; but it cannot take into account all the local peculiarities—the hills or river estuary—that play such an important part in weather conditions in our own home town.

By careful observation and a knowledge of the basic principles of meteorology, it is possible to find absorbing interest in the local applications of weather lore. But meteorology is a science, and as such it needs a degree of persistence and patient study before a proper understanding can be reached.

Nature has provided ways and means of making accurate observations on the state of the air. Added to local barometer and other meteorological readings these facts enable us to assess present weather conditions and to forecast what to expect in future. Most of the old weather saws are the result of accumulated experience by that most accurate of observers—the countryman. Many are capable of scientific explanation; some are quite unfounded in fact and almost worthless.

At the seaside a piece of seaweed will warn of impending rain by appearing damp. Seaweed contains small quantities of chemical salts, among which is one that has the ability to take up water from the air—if there is plenty of moisture available. This makes the seaweed damp when the air is full of moisture—and air in this state needs only a little cooling to lose some of its water as rain.

" Clear moon, frost soon." A clear moon is seen when there are no clouds in the night sky. Cloud acts as a blanket that prevents heat radiating rapidly from the earth at night. When there is little cloud the earth cools quickly; hence the frost.

" Red sky at night " is caused by light rays which are split up as they pass through air containing fairly large floating particles—water droplets, dust, and soot. This may mean that there has not been a high wind to blow these particles away. Calm conditions of this sort often appear with a region of high pressure over the country. High pressure brings good weather, so that red sky at night is the shepherd's delight.

In the morning there is rarely much soot in the air; a red sky then means that light is being scattered by droplets of water in the lower atmosphere instead. This usually means rain.

There is a limitless variety of traditional methods of predicting weather; each local district has its own. For anyone who wants an insight into the mysteries of scientific method there is no better hobby than a study of the behaviour of the atmosphere as it manifests itself in what we call the weather. It is a good thing for the scientist, too, to find how little he really knows about the sea of gas in which he lives.

The pressure of the air at any point on the earth's surface is in a state of constant change. Where pressure is high the air will tend to flow downwards and out-wards into regions where air pressure is low. As the air sinks down in the high-pressure area it is compressed and warmed, so that a region of high pressure is generally associated with warm, dry weather.

Where pressure is low air flows in from areas of higher pressure near by. As it flows into the low-pressure region the air expands and is, in consequence, cooled. If it is saturated with moisture it is less able to hold the moisture as it cools. Low-pressure areas, there-fore, bring cold and rainy weather.

Although the air over the entire surface of the earth is always flowing from high- to low-pressure regions, there are three areas where great masses of air are in a state of constant turmoil. These are regions where the major wind systems of the world converge and clash.

The north-easterly trade winds flow from the Northern Hemisphere towards the equator; here, in the region of the doldrums, they meet the south-easterlies from the Southern Hemisphere. In the low-pressure area of the doldrums the two great wind systems clash; up into the atmosphere soars a vast stream of warm, moist air. As it rises it cools and throws out water as rain that pours in a deluge over tropical lands. This zone of bad weather round the centre of the earth is called the Equatorial Convergence.

In the middle latitudes of both the northern and southern hemispheres are the Polar Fronts, where winds and rainstorms also mark the meeting place of huge masses of moving air. Flowing down from the frozen poles a layer of cold, heavy air creeps over the surface of the earth. As it meets the warm, moist air of the westerlies the cold air thrusts the warm air aloft where it expands and cools, throwing out its moisture as mist and rain. The boundary of the mass of polar air is constantly on the move; long fingers of cold air push down towards the equator, bringing winds and storms as the air blows rapidly from place to place. With the jet stream marking out the meeting-place of cold and warm air in the upper layer of the troposphere, the cold front drifts over large areas of the middle latitudes.

In the Northern Hemisphere the disturbances associated with the Polar Front bring changeable weather to the west coasts of Europe and the United States. Caught up in the westerly flow of air that blows in these latitudes, the ' highs ' and ' lows ' drift over the Pacific and Atlantic. Winds blowing between the areas of different pressure bring weather that is never settled for very long.

The traditional British weather is steady and unexciting in that it does not go to great extremes; but its day-to-day antics are a constant source of indignation and surprise. The prevailing winds over Britain are from the west. They blow across a large expanse of warm Atlantic Ocean, and when they arrive over Britain they are warm and wet. It is this steady flow of westerly wind that gives Britain an equable climate. British winters are mild compared with those in Central

Europe; British summers are seldom remarkable for the high temperatures they produce.

Having provided this mild, phlegmatic sort of climate, Nature arranged that the pressure disturbances associated with the Polar Front should sustain the changeableness which has made British weather so unique. Britain is placed fairly and squarely in the path of a continual stream of atmospheric pressure mêlées which drift in mainly from the Atlantic. As air flows from a region of high pressure to a region of lower pressure, it does not flow directly between the two; it tends to flow in spiral fashion like water flowing from a bath. As a high- or low-pressure system drifts over the British Isles, therefore, the wind directions can change rapidly depending on the positions of the high and low pressure regions. As the wind brings weather with it, the weather can change radically from day to day. Such is Britain's geographical position that the continual movement of the 'highs' and 'lows' makes only one thing certain about British weather—it will not remain steady for long.

By placing the British Isles in a unique position on the globe Nature intensified the effects of the ever-changing wind directions associated with the pressure systems. Clinging to the edge of Europe, the British Isles are sandwiched between the largest land mass in the world—the combined continents of Europe and Asia—and the great expanse of the Atlantic Ocean. Blowing from a westerly direction, the wind is from the ocean; blowing from the east, it may have travelled over thousands of miles of land. Each direction has a characteristic effect on the weather that is carried by the wind.

The world receives a constant supply of energy in the form of sunshine. Where the sunshine falls on the surface of the earth it provides heat. But the earth is also losing heat by radiation throughout the entire twenty-four hours of the day. It is the balance between heat coming in and heat going out that determines the temperature at any place on the earth's surface. If there is more heat coming in than there is going out the surface will warm up; if there is more heat going out than there is coming in—for example, at night, when there is no sunshine—then the earth will cool.

Water and land affect this energy balance in different ways. The sea is transparent to sunlight, so that heat from the sun is absorbed through a considerable depth of water. Also, more heat is needed to raise the temperature of water than to warm up solid earth. The sunshine heats the sea slowly and to a great depth; conversely, the sea loses its heat very gradually by radiation.

The land, on the other hand, is opaque to sunlight. Most of the heat from sunshine is developed on the surface of the earth; it does not penetrate to any depth. As a consequence the land heats quickly; and when the sun goes down at night it cools quickly as well.

In general, an ocean acts as a huge reservoir of heat in which the temperature changes very slowly. A land mass, on the other hand, heats and cools rapidly, depending on the amount of sunshine it is receiving.

The British Isles lie on a boundary between these two fundamentally different climatic influences. Off the west coast is an enormous bath of water which is warmed by the Gulf Stream flowing from the Gulf of Mexico. This current of warm water carries in it heat from the sunshine that shone on the water of the Caribbean Sea. It warms the Atlantic waters off the coast of Britain throughout the year.

On the other side of the British Isles there is the vast land-mass of Europe and Asia. In winter, when there is little warmth in the sunshine, radiation of heat from the land is apt to get the upper hand. In the centre of the land-mass—in Russia—winters are often severe. In summer things are apt to go to the other extreme and weather can be uncomfortably hot.

As pressure systems bring their swirling winds over Western Europe the weather that is blown in is greatly influenced by the effects of these masses of land and water. British weather can be classified into definite types depending on the relative positions of the high- and low-pressure areas that are in the vicinity of Western Europe.

In Type 1 the area of low pressure—the depression— is occupying its familiar position over Iceland; the high-pressure area is over the Azores. This is the commonest of the pressure systems; on average it represents the atmospheric state in one day out of every three in Britain. During winter it accounts for half of all our weather. Type 1 pressure system is characterized by warmth and moisture which is blown from the Atlantic by westerly winds. As it rises over the hills the air cools and deposits its moisture as rain or drizzle.

In Type 2 the depression has detached itself from Iceland and is now off the north-east coast of Scotland. The high-pressure area has moved correspondingly and is off the south coast or Land's End. The wind is flowing from the north-west. This system prevails about once a week on the average through the year, with a preference for July. As the wind is blowing from polar regions instead of from the warm Atlantic bath, it is liable to be cold. In winter Type 2 brings snow and thunderstorms. It also causes the beautiful winter days when the air is clean and clear; it has not had an opportunity of picking up smoke or dirt. Type 2 is responsible for the most exhilarating of winter weather. In summer the north-west wind will often bring cool showers at first, with fine weather later.

As the depression moves to the east coast of Britain,

with the high-pressure area off the west of Ireland, the wind blows from the north. This is Type 3 pressure system, which appears on average about once a fortnight. Again, Type 3 brings a cold polar wind, carrying the severest of all British weather.

> The north wind doth blow,
> And we shall have snow.

Fortunately this Type 3 weather comes only rarely during the winter.

In Type 4 the depression is lying off the Kentish coast, with the high-pressure area near the Hebrides or to the north of Scotland. The wind is blowing north-east or east; coming from northern Europe, it is again liable to be cold. This sort of weather often comes in spring and early summer. It is the weather that is so unpopular with the fruit-growers; it brings the sharp frosty spells that can ruin the blossom on the trees. Once it has set in it tends to persist. This Type 4 weather reverses the usual order of things; the winds bring rain and clouds to the east coast, and the west coast has a welcome respite.

In winter the north-east winds are often dry as well as cold; they will absorb moisture rapidly when they blow across our hands and faces, causing additional chilling as a result of the evaporation. These winds are noted for their ' bite.'

In Type 5 the depression is lying off the Cornish coast, with the high-pressure area over Scandinavia. The wind is south-east. In spring and autumn this type of weather appears, on the average, once a week; during summer it is uncommon. When it does come during summer it blows over a hot land-mass, bringing sub-tropical weather. In autumn it brings a welcome Indian summer.

These five types of pressure system cover, very broadly, the various positions of high- and low-pressure areas that affect the British Isles. But, in addition, the centre of high or low pressure may be directly overhead.

Once a week on average there is a high-pressure area over Britain. This is the anticyclone that brings quiet weather conditions. In summer the weather is fine and warm; it is often settled and may persist and cause a drought. In winter Type 6 weather is not so popular; it often leaves a blanket of fog.

Finally, in Type 7 an area of low pressure is hovering over Britain. This is the depression that often means gales around the coasts and heavy rain; in summer it tends to bring thunderstorms. After Type 1 this Type 7 system is the most common of all. One day in five is a depression day during the winter.

In these main types of weather systems, with all their modifications, Britain is able to enjoy almost every form of weather throughout the year. Switching rapidly from one type to another, Nature makes the most of her opportunities; the life of the weather-forecaster in Britain is seldom dull.

6

Life-giving Oxygen

FEW things have affected the course of history so profoundly as did the discovery of fire. Fire enabled man to keep himself warm as he penetrated into colder lands; fire cooked his food and scared away marauding beasts; it opened the way to countless industries and crafts, helping man to graduate from stone to bronze and from bronze to iron and eventually to all the modern metals and materials. Small wonder that in the early days of civilization fire became an object of mystery and worship.

The flickering flame was something that the philosophers of old found difficulty in understanding. Ancient Greeks believed that fire was one of the four elements from which all other forms of matter were derived. This material theory of fire persisted through the centuries; it was not until the late eighteenth century that scientists began to identify fire and flames with chemical changes. In 1783 the famous French chemist Antoine Lavoisier showed that fire was not in itself a material thing; it was a manifestation of chemical change between the burning substance and the oxygen gas in the air.

Oxygen, which makes up one-fifth of the atmosphere, is an active chemical. Atoms of oxygen will join forces with atoms of almost every other element, forming ' compound atoms,' or molecules of new substances. Water, for example, is a result of the union between one atom of oxygen and two of hydrogen; eight-ninths of the weight of all the water on earth is oxygen. Oxygen is present in almost every rock and mineral; in sand and silica, clay and limestone, granite and chalk, oxygen is united with other elements. Half the weight of the rocks in the crust of the earth comes from oxygen. It is the most abundant element of all.

In the atmosphere oxygen gas exists in the free state, uncombined with other elements. Its atoms are chemically independent of the atoms and molecules of nitrogen and other gases of the air. The particles of all these atmospheric gases are simply mixed together; they are not grouped into compound atoms such as would happen if they underwent chemical union. They can, in consequence, be separated easily from one another.

This store of free oxygen in the atmosphere acts as a reservoir from which oxygen reaches the innumerable processes involved in life and living. Oxygen, by its eagerness to take part in chemical changes, is in a state of constant movement between the atmosphere and the living and inanimate things on earth.

When anything burns in air some of its constituent elements are combining with the oxygen of the air to form new substances. The flame is the region in which the chemical reaction is taking place; the heat of the flame is energy liberated as a result of the chemical changes.

Most of the fuels we burn deliberately on earth as a source of heat are materials containing supplies of the element carbon. Carbon plays a major role in the structure of all living things. Animals and plants are built up very largely from carbon in combination with hydrogen, nitrogen, and a few other elements. Most of the thousands of intricate chemical changes that are involved in life are taking place between compounds containing a high proportion of carbon. These substances are what are described as organic materials; most of them, by virtue of the carbon they contain, will burn in air. As they burn the carbon combines with oxygen of the air, forming carbon dioxide gas, and hydrogen that was present in the organic substance unites with oxygen to form water. The association of one atom of carbon with two of oxygen to yield the compound molecule of carbon dioxide results in an overflow of energy, and heat is liberated. This heat, together with that released by the union of hydrogen and oxygen atoms as they form water, is the heat that scorches a moth's wings in a candle flame or turns boiler water into steam or warms our living-rooms in winter.

The stored fuels that we use so lavishly as our energy sources to-day are little more than stores of carbon and hydrogen that can be united conveniently with atmospheric oxygen. Coal is the compressed and concentrated remains of plants that lived when the world was young. Inside it are stored the carbon-containing chemicals created by the plants as they flourished and grew. Burned in the kitchen grate or in the industrial furnace, the coal gives up these chemicals as a source of heat energy. Their carbon combines with oxygen in the air that flows through the burning coal, forming carbon dioxide gas that disappears up the chimney; hydrogen associated with carbon in the coal is similarly burned to water. The heat given out during these chemical changes is used to warm the boiler or the room.

Oil is a store of carbon chemicals of a different sort, formed from the bodies of billions of tiny sea creatures that lived in bygone days. From the carbon and hydrogen in these prehistoric graveyards we derive the heat energy that is liberated when oil burns in air.

Coal and oil are concentrated stores of once-living matter and are, in consequence, particularly valuable as fuels. But almost every form of plant or animal matter can burn in air. Wood and peat, flesh and muscle, will all burn as their carbon and hydrogen combine with oxygen in the air to form carbon dioxide and water.

An immense variety of different carbon chemicals is involved in the chemical interchanges of living matter. Modern industrial techniques enable us to separate and modify these chemicals, for example by distillation to provide fuels that are suitable for specific needs. When coal is heated in coke ovens some of its carbon-containing chemicals are driven off in the form of coal gas; others distil as liquid chemicals that are used as raw material by the chemical industry; some of the carbon remains in the retort as coke.

Crude oil is distilled and split into well-defined mixtures of carbon chemicals. Some are ' cracked ' and ' reformed ' to change them into chemicals that are suited to definite jobs. But in whatever way these coal- or oil-derived chemicals eventually serve as fuels, the basic process is normally the same; carbon and hydrogen unite with oxygen from the air.

When fuels are burned the progress of the chemical change is controlled by limiting the supply of either the fuel or the air. The flame of a gas ring is the zone in which gas is combining with oxygen of the air, producing carbon dioxide and water. The size of the flame is adjusted by controlling the amount of gas that leaves the tube. The fire in a modern grate is damped down by limiting the supply of air that reaches it from below; the coal burns fiercely if the air supply is increased. When a fuel is intimately mixed with the oxygen it needs to burn, and the mixture is ignited, chemical reaction between the fuel and the oxygen can take place instantaneously. A tremendous volume of carbon dioxide gas and steam is produced, the gases being expanded rapidly by the heat liberated during the reaction. The result is an explosion.

Combustible materials such as flour or coal dust floating in the air can explode violently in this way; mills have been wrecked and mine workings destroyed by the explosive burning of flour or coal-dust in the air.

Instantaneous combustion of a fuel is used to provide power in the motor-car engine. Petrol vapour is mixed with air in the carburettor, and the mixture is drawn into the cylinders of the engine. Inside the engine the mixture is sparked; this starts the chemical reaction between the fuel and the oxygen of the air. Carbon dioxide and steam are formed in a fraction of a second as the mixture burns; expanded by the heat released during the chemical reaction, the gases push the piston down and drive the car along. Oxygen from the air is just as much a fuel for the car as is the petrol, and the ordinary petrol engine will operate only where the atmosphere can supply it with the air it needs. Where planes are flying high and the air is thin extra supplies are forced into the engine with the help of super-chargers. In the jet engine air is drawn in at the front, mixed with fuel, and burned, and enormous volumes of hot expanding gas are forced from the rear. They provide the thrust that drives the plane along.

As we approach the boundaries of space the tenuous air is unable to supply the oxygen needed to burn fuel in an engine. The machine abandons the atmosphere as its oxygen source and has to carry its own supplies. The rocket takes over from the ordinary engine as a power unit.

In a rocket all the materials needed for producing enormous quantities of hot gas are carried as fuel. The rocket is independent of the oxygen in the air and can operate as well in space as it does in the atmosphere.

The V2 rocket, for example, carried alcohol as its fuel, together with five tons of liquid oxygen. When the rocket was fired alcohol and oxygen were mixed and ignited. Carbon and hydrogen of the alcohol united so rapidly with the oxygen that 130,000 cubic feet of gas were formed during the minute that the fuel was burning.

In explosives the principle is the same. Carbon, hydrogen, and other combustible materials may be mixed intimately with oxygen or chemicals that can supply oxygen. Given a suitable stimulus, chemical reaction between the oxygen and the combustible substances takes place. Great quantities of heated gas are formed instantaneously in a confined space, and the expanding gas overcomes all opposition in its way.

Gunpowder contains carbon and sulphur, both of which will burn in oxygen to form gas; mixed with the carbon and sulphur is potassium nitrate, a chemical that contains a lot of oxygen. When the gunpowder explodes the potassium nitrate provides oxygen needed by the carbon and sulphur for instantaneous gas-production.

Wood charcoal, sawdust, soot, and other sources of carbon can burn with explosive violence if the oxygen they need is available to them in the necessary quantity. Explosives of this type are used in mining and tunnelling; the carbon is packed into cartridges which are soaked in liquid oxygen before being put into the bore-hole. The cartridge is fired electrically, exploding without producing any gas more harmful than carbon dioxide. These explosives are more than twice as effective as blasting gelatine and have the great advantage of losing their power if they fail to explode. The liquid oxygen evaporates and leaves a harmless carbon cartridge.

In the plant and animal worlds carbon-containing substances are burned in atmospheric oxygen to provide the energy needed to sustain life. Within the leaves of all green plants carbon dioxide from the air and water from the soil are manufactured into sugar. Energy from the sunshine is absorbed and stored away as chemical energy inside the sugar; this is the source of the energy we derive from coal and oil and similar fuels; it is the energy in the plant food on which we depend for life.

In the plant sugar is distributed to the living cells and used as fuel whenever it is needed. With the help of oxygen that diffuses into the plant the sugar 'burns'; its carbon unites with oxygen to form carbon dioxide once again, and its hydrogen finishes up as water. The energy liberated is used by living processes of the cell. Sugar is the main energy-yielding material of the plant world. Oxygen is the key that releases the energy as it is needed.

In animals and human beings this same energy-liberating process is at work. The food we eat consists very largely of carbon-containing substances manufactured for us by the plant world. Sugars, fats, and proteins are all carbon chemicals in which is locked away energy taken by plants from the sunshine as they built up sugars and other substances from carbon dioxide and water. Inside the body oxygen helps us to reverse the process, turning the carbon and hydrogen back into carbon dioxide and water and liberating energy in the process. When we breathe we are taking in supplies of atmospheric oxygen which are used for burning the fuel that comes from our food. The process of respiration is basically the same as that which delivers heat in a factory boiler or in a kitchen stove.

In the plant world air needed for burning up sugar diffuses into the living cells. But in a structure as large and complex as the human body an intricate transport system has to be used to carry oxygen to all outlying districts.

Air needed by the human furnace is brought into the body through the lungs. In the lungs the air enters a network of fine cells and passages in which it is separated from an intricate system of slender blood-vessels by a flimsy membrane. In human beings the lungs contain some 700 million of these tiny air chambers; the surface area amounts to more than 2000 square feet.

Through this vast surface the air is able to pass supplies of oxygen to the blood circulating in the network of fine vessels. The amount of oxygen which can actually dissolve in the liquid part of the blood is quite small; if we had to depend on dissolved oxygen we should need sixteen times our normal quantity of blood. Instead of burdening us with this great volume of blood, Nature has provided an oxygen-carrying system that can absorb the supplies we need even though the volume of liquid is comparatively small.

Floating in the liquid portion of the blood, the plasma, there are tiny corpuscles containing the red hæmoglobin that gives the blood its colour. This iron-containing pigment can carry oxygen by combining loosely with it to form the substance oxyhæmoglobin, and in this way oxygen is distributed to every part of the body.

As it reaches the living tissues the blood releases supplies of oxygen from its oxyhæmoglobin to the lymph that bathes the active cells. From the lymph oxygen is passed into the interior of the cells, where it takes part in energy-liberating reactions with the organic substances that have come in the first place from the carbon chemicals eaten as food.

As the carbon of these substances unites with the oxygen carbon dioxide is formed, and water from the hydrogen. Carbon dioxide diffuses from the cell to the lymph and then to the blood. It is carried back to the lungs and eventually exhaled.

This interchange of gases is maintained by the lungs throughout the life of every human being. Like other bodily processes, it is able to adjust itself to meet the changing needs of the tissues. A healthy adult breathes at a rate of fourteen to eighteen times a minute under normal circumstances, and about a pint of oxygen is taken up by the blood. But if the body is needing energy to provide for violent exercise or work more air is needed; the lungs expand and contract more fully, taking in three or four times the normal amount of air, and the breathing rate increases until oxygen is being absorbed at a rate of six pints a minute. To carry the extra supplies of oxygen the blood must circulate more quickly; with the body at rest the lungs are washed by six to fourteen pints of blood per minute, but to cope with violent exercise the blood may flow through the tiny capillaries at a rate of sixty pints per minute.

This breathing system used by man has been devised to meet the circumstances in which he normally lives. The lungs are tuned to operate at the bottom of an ocean of air under a pressure of 14½ lb. to the square inch. But if man changes his environment in such a way that he is living in air at a different pressure the body can adapt itself to operate under the abnormal pressure.

In the upper layers of the troposphere the air is thin and its pressure is lower than at ground level. Mountain climbers are often attacked by sickness and violent headaches; they become irritable and are unable to think rationally.

Given a chance the body can do a lot to acclimatize itself to thin-air conditions. The Everest expedition allowed sufficient time during the ascent for the bodies of the climbers to become adjusted to the lower pressure of air at high altitudes. In some communities, such as mining villages situated high up in the Andes, people acquire an acclimatization that is virtually permanent.

To provide itself with oxygen from low-pressure air the body increases the amount of air entering the lungs by more adequate breathing, and also provides more hæmoglobin so that the blood can carry bigger supplies of oxygen. At the same time it modifies the hæmoglobin in such a way that its ability to pick up oxygen is improved. Tests have shown that blood containing 4.9 million red corpuscles per cubic mm. at sea-level will contain 5.4 million after a week at a height of 14,000 feet and 5.75 million after three weeks. The oxygen-carrying capacity of the blood during the three weeks acclimatization increases by more than a quarter.

Where human beings are living in an atmosphere with a pressure greater than normal the body is subjected to a different kind of stress. Divers work in an atmosphere that may be at three or four times the normal pressure. At such pressures the gases in the air will dissolve more copiously in the blood plasma and other body liquids. This has no immediate ill-effects at ordinary diving pressures, but as the diver rises to the lower pressure of the atmosphere the dissolved gases find their way out of the body fluids. If decompression is too rapid the gases—particularly nitrogen—appear as tiny bubbles in the body, carrying the sickness, paralysis, and severe pain associated with the ' bends.' This can be avoided by allowing the diver to return slowly to normal pressure, when the gases are given a chance to find their way harmlessly from the blood. As atmospheric gases are particularly soluble in fats, diving is a job that is unsuitable for stout people.

In many elementary forms of animal life the arrangements made for absorbing oxygen are quite simple. The primitive amœba, floating in water like a speck of jelly, absorbs its oxygen by the most direct route. Oxygen diffuses through the entire surface of the amœba's body into the tissues that are needing it; carbon dioxide diffuses from the amœba in a similar way. This process operates even in some of the higher animals; a frog, for example, does a lot of breathing through its skin. It can survive for several days without using its lungs, but will suffocate quickly if its skin is sealed up.

Insects have developed a breathing system that is all their own. They have no lungs or circulatory system to carry oxygen throughout their bodies. Instead they rely on a network of very fine tubes, which carry air direct to the cells that are needing it. This system is of limited efficiency and will operate only over very short distances. It has proved a severe stumbling block to insect development, keeping insect bodies small. A large insect could not supply itself with the air it needs; the tubes would be too long to allow the air to penetrate to the interior tissues.

Fishes and creatures of the sea are no less dependent than are animals on atmospheric oxygen for their source of energy. Oxygen dissolves in seawater and is stripped from the water by the gills of the fish. As water passes through gills it bathes the extensive surfaces of thin membranes similar to those inside a lung. Oxygen diffuses through the membranes into the blood beneath.

Although atmospheric oxygen is intensely active and eager to undergo all sorts of chemical change, it is continually hampered and restrained by the nitrogen that dilutes it in the air. Only a fifth of the air is oxygen; the nitrogen that makes up most of the remainder is an inert and unresponsive gas. Where oxygen is alive and vigorous nitrogen is chemically dead. It takes no part in the chemical changes supported by oxygen, and by diluting the oxygen it acts as a damper on its partner's activity.

In respiration, combustion, and all the other changes in which oxygen plays a part the intensity of the processes can be heightened by increasing the concentration of oxygen that is available. By adding pure oxygen to the air we breathe we can supply the tissues more readily with the oxygen they need, and their activity increases. Extra oxygen is given to patients who find difficulty in absorbing enough oxygen from the air.

In industry air is used in tremendous quantities as a source of oxygen. When fuel is burned oxygen in the air is a raw material; in metal-smelting and purification atmospheric oxygen helps to burn away impurities; in the chemical industry oxygen is imprisoned in innumerable chemicals. Wherever air is being used as a source of oxygen in this way nitrogen is interfering with the activity of the oxygen. By enriching the air with added supplies of oxygen or by using oxygen itself in place of air we can often raise the efficiency of industrial processes to a remarkable degree. As a result oxygen has become an industrial raw material of increasing importance during recent years.

The manufacture of pure oxygen has itself become an industry, and the development of processes for making oxygen cheaply and in bulk now ranks as one of the great industrial achievements of our time.

The method used for making oxygen was devised half a century ago. Air is compressed to about 3000 pounds per square inch, and the carbon dioxide and water are removed from it. After it has cooled the compressed air is allowed to expand. The effect of expansion is to cool the air still further, and this cold air is used to cool incoming air; this in its turn is allowed to expand and cool to an even lower temperature. By successive step-wise cooling in this way the air eventually becomes so cold that it liquefies.

When liquid air is distilled the more volatile nitrogen evaporates first, leaving oxygen behind. The two gases can be separated easily and efficiently; they are now produced in thousands of millions of cubic feet a year, each more than 99 per cent. pure.

For many years the industrial use of oxygen was restricted by the cost of storing and distributing the gas. Compressed into the familiar steel cylinders, it was heavy and expensive to handle. Shortly before World War II techniques were developed for carrying and storing liquid oxygen in insulated road and rail tank wagons, and cheap oxygen became available in bulk to industries that could make good use of it.

Much of the output of oxygen at that time was absorbed by the oxy-acetylene techniques used for cutting and welding steel and other metals. During the war, shipbuilding and armaments industries made heavy demands on the oxygen industry; output increased and the manufacturing processes became more efficient. Equipment was designed to provide oxygen where it was needed, cutting out the cost and difficulties of transport. Oxygen generators weighing little more than a hundredweight were used to provide oxygen in high-flying planes. As flying became faster and planes flew higher the need for oxygen has increased steadily to the present day. Oxygen is now a major requirement of the armed forces.

Modern aircraft carriers need no longer carry tons of metal cylinders to provide the oxygen that is needed for their planes. Each ship can be fitted with equipment for liquefying air and distilling it to separate oxygen and nitrogen. The nitrogen is used as an inert, non-inflammable atmosphere in fuel pipes and tanks; the oxygen provides for the needs of the high-flying pilots.

Equipment of this sort may weigh 10 tons or more, but it manufactures in a fortnight as much oxygen as would otherwise be carried in 100 tons of cylinders.

In submarines a new technique has been developed for providing oxygen needed by the crew. Although a submerged submarine is cut off from supplies of atmospheric oxygen, it is floating in unlimited quantities of oxygen combined with hydrogen in the form of water. A process has been devised for splitting seawater into its constituent elements and using the oxygen to provide the atmosphere needed by the crew. This novel method of generating oxygen in submarines is based on well-established principles; electricity is passed through seawater containing a small amount of a chemical. From two and a half pints of water enough oxygen can be generated to provide the daily needs of one member of the crew.

Since the end of the war developments in manufacturing and storage techniques have made oxygen into a cheap and abundant raw material for industry. And as a result the demand for oxygen has been increasing at an astounding rate.

The old-established oxy-acetylene flame is now at work all over the world, and it is becoming ever more versatile. The 7500° F. flame can cut through steel more than a foot thick; it can weld and clean the surfaces of metals. Steel is now descaled, for example, by heating its surface with an oxy-acetylene flame. Expanding suddenly in the fierce heat of the flame, the scale flies off leaving the fresh steel surface ready for painting. Metal surfaces can be covered with thin continuous coatings of plastic by feeding plastic powder into an oxy-acetylene flame; the powder melts instantaneously and sticks to the metal surface. In the next decade or so oxygen will find its biggest outlet as a raw material in the production of iron and steel. Air is one of the essential raw materials in iron and steel manufacture; now that oxygen is becoming cheap and plentiful it shows signs of taking over from air.

In the blast furnace iron ore is smelted into pig iron with the help of coke, limestone, and air. Blown in at the base of the towering furnace, air sweeps up through a mass of these materials, providing oxygen that is needed to burn the coke and build up the terrific heat inside the furnace. But the blast of heated, compressed air is mostly nitrogen, which serves no useful purpose in the furnace.

The weight of air blown through the blast furnace is greater than that of all the other raw materials. And the unwanted nitrogen it contains is more than just an irritating source of inefficiency; it plays a major role in the entire design and operation of the iron-making process. Because the air blast contains so much nitrogen, the reactions involving oxygen in the furnace are slower than they otherwise would be. In order to do its work the air must therefore pass through a great depth of material inside the furnace. This is one of the main reasons for the embarrassing height of the blast furnace, which may reach 100 feet or more. As a result of this great height the pressure at the base of the furnace charge is immense. The raw materials used, particularly the coke, must be sufficiently strong to withstand the pressure without collapsing into an impermeable mass. Providing high-strength coke is one of the greatest problems faced by every iron industry in the world. Suitable coke can be made only from certain types of coal, and the siting of blast furnaces is often controlled by the availability of metallurgical coke.

But the effect of nitrogen in the air blast goes still further. Air is heated before it enters the furnace, and much of this heat is wasted in warming up the nitrogen. Huge burners are needed to heat the enormous volumes of air, and special blowers must be provided to force the air into the base of the furnace. The gases coming from the top of the furnace are diluted with all the nitrogen that entered at the base; without this nitrogen they could be an invaluable fuel.

The effect of using oxygen instead of air can therefore influence the operation of a blast furnace in many ways. Without the deadening nitrogen there would no longer be a need for furnaces of tremendous height; the reactions in the furnace would be completed much more quickly. Smaller furnaces would be simpler to build and maintain. Equipment for heating great volumes of ingoing gas would no longer be required. Gases coming from the furnace top would be a useful fuel.

Most important of all, with only the pressure of a small column of ore and other materials to withstand inside the furnace the coke would not need the strength that is essential in a normal furnace. And with a more efficient reaction going on inside the furnace the process would be able to operate effectively on ores that are nowadays regarded as too poor to use.

The overall effect of using oxygen in place of air in the blast furnace could be revolutionary. No longer would the production of iron be threatened by shortage of suitable coke or high-grade ore as it is to-day. In Britain deposits of low-grade ore would become available for iron production, and we should no longer be dependent on imported, high-grade ore. Huge reserves of coal would become suitable for steel production in place of the restricted supplies of special coking coal on which we now rely.

Inevitably there are many difficulties in the way of switching over quickly to the general use of oxygen in place of air. Only really cheap, bulk supplies of oxygen could make it possible, and the quantities involved would be tremendous. It would have to compete with

Photo The British Oxygen Co., Ltd.

LIQUID OXYGEN TANKERS

The tank on the right holds eighty tons of liquid oxygen.

Photo Imperial War Museum

A V2 ROCKET LEAVING ITS
LAUNCHING PLATFORM

Alcohol burns with the help of five
tons of liquid oxygen.

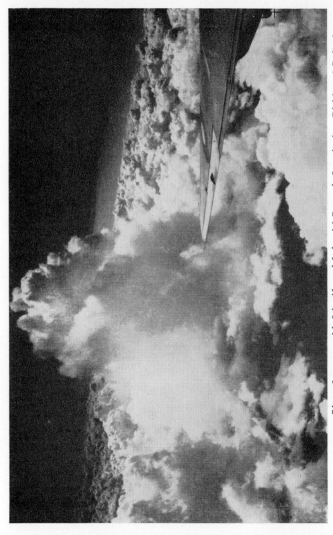

Photo Commonwealth Scientific and Industrial Research Organization, Division of Radiophysics

CLOUD-SEEDING TO PRODUCE RAIN

The first man-made rainstorm in the world produced under controlled conditions occurred near Sydney, in February 1947. One of a number of small, individual clouds was treated with dry ice, and subsequently rained. No others in the vicinity did so. This photograph shows the cloud-development thirteen minutes after seeding.

air, which is free. Moreover, oxygen enrichment of the blast would render obsolete much of the plant that serves the modern iron and steel industry. Even the geographical situation of the steel plants would be affected by the change in the balance of raw materials.

But in spite of the difficulties the change must in time be made. The advantages are so great that they cannot be denied. In Russia the iron and steel industry is believed to have begun a large-scale conversion to the use of oxygen in 1947. New steel plants in the Donbas and Soviet Asia were being built at a cost of the equivalent of £500 million; the blast furnaces were to operate on oxygen produced in specially designed equipment. It has been reported that, with the help of oxygen, Russia has reduced the cost of steel production by a quarter or more.

In Britain a great deal of experimental work has been carried out on the oxygen blast. At Liège, in Belgium, nine countries, including Britain, have combined in a project sponsored by the Organisation for European Economic Co-operation to study the operation of a pilot blast furnace using oxygen instead of air. More than 50 tons of oxygen a day is fed to the furnace from a generating plant.

At Liège the advantages of the oxygen process are being balanced against the many factors that would be involved in a major change to new technique.

In other stages of steel manufacture oxygen is showing equally impressive advantages over air as a raw material. In the open hearth steel furnace oxygen can halve the time needed to produce a batch of steel. Mixed with the air blast in a Bessemer converter, oxygen can double the amount of scrap used in each charge. Russian scientists have claimed that oxygen can reduce the time of blast from fifteen minutes to one minute.

In other industries cheap oxygen is settling down to

many new jobs. At Brownsville, in Texas, one of the world's biggest oxygen plants is helping to produce synthetic petrol from natural gas. The successful development of the underground gasification of coal may turn in the end on the availability of low-cost oxygen. Forced into the seam of burning coal, oxygen helps to decompose the coal into gaseous products that can be piped up to the surface. Already gasification is believed to be working economically in Russia; experimental installations are operating in Belgium, Britain, and other countries.

Many of these applications of oxygen in industry could lead to demands for astronomical quantities of oxygen in the future. Rocket fuels, iron and steel, and coal gasification alone could create an oxygen industry many times as large as that which exists to-day.

7

The Lethargy of Nitrogen

In September 1772 a young student at Edinburgh University presented his thesis for the degree of M.D. The student, Daniel Rutherford, described how he had enclosed air in an apparatus and used up the active part of the air by burning carbon in it or by letting animals breathe in it. After absorbing the carbon dioxide that was formed in this way Rutherford found that a lot of air remained. It would support no further combustion or respiration, and he called it 'noxious air.' This was the gas we now know as nitrogen.

Unlike oxygen, its atmospheric partner, nitrogen will not easily combine with other elements. It is passive and inert. Yet nitrogen plays a vital role in the activities of every form of life on earth. It is present in all the proteins, the complex substances that are the life-supporting materials of plants and animals.

Inside every living cell proteins form much of the protoplasm, the jelly-like substance that sustains the life of the cell and, ultimately, of the entire living organism. More than half of the weight of the human body, excluding water, is protein. Muscle and flesh, skin and bone, cartilage and blood, are all built up with the help of protein. No matter what form it takes all protein contains nitrogen in its chemical structure: nitrogen that has come originally from the enormous reservoir of nitrogen in the air.

Above every square mile of the earth's surface twenty

million tons of nitrogen are available as a raw material for the manufacture of living matter. Yet living things cannot draw directly on this atmospheric nitrogen for their needs. Human beings and other animals are unable to absorb their nitrogen supplies from the air drawn into their lungs, as they do the oxygen. Plants cannot take their nitrogen from the air that permeates their leaves. The animal world derives the nitrogen for its protein from food, and to serve as raw material for protein-building in the body the nitrogen in the food of the animal world must normally be in the form of ready-made protein substances or their chemical relatives. We human beings cannot build our nitrogen-containing proteins for ourselves from nitrogen; we leave someone else to do the protein-building and then make use of these proteins in our food. We rearrange and modify these food proteins in our bodies, suiting them to the purposes for which they are needed. Our supplies of food proteins come from the animal protein in meat and fish, milk and eggs, or from the plant protein in bread and potatoes, peas and beans, and other vegetable products.

Ultimately plants supply all the protein used by animals as food. Human beings, for example, eat food provided by plants or eat animals that have in turn made use of plants as food.

In their ability to construct the complex proteins and similar substances from simple starting materials plants are more efficient chemical machines than are animals. Plants cannot depend upon any other level of living things to make their proteins for them. They must carry out the chemical construction work for themselves, using raw materials available to them in the soil and in the air.

If nitrogen was not so chemically inactive the plant might have devised a way of drawing its supplies directly from the air. In every plant air is flowing constantly through the millions of pores that puncture the surfaces of the leaves; as it finds its way between the spongy mass of cells inside the leaf the air gives up its carbon dioxide to provide the carbon needed by the plant. But the stolid, inactive nitrogen flows out from the leaf unchanged, just as it is breathed out by human beings after we have made use of the oxygen in the air.

How, then, does atmospheric nitrogen find its way from the air into the plant, yielding itself up as raw material for combination with carbon, hydrogen, oxygen, and other elements that make up the living protein?

The point of entry is the soil. In the soil atmospheric nitrogen is united with oxygen and other elements to form simple chemicals such as nitrates. These chemicals dissolve in the water of the soil and are absorbed as solutions into the roots of plants. Flowing upward through the sap vessels of the plant, the solutions of nitrogen and other chemicals reach the leaves and growing centres where they act as raw materials for making proteins.

The critical point in this flow of atmospheric nitrogen into the plant via the soil lies in the chemical capture of the gas and its imprisonment in the form of simple chemicals in the soil. Much of the credit for this achievement goes to the micro-organisms that inhabit every fertile soil. Many types of soil bacteria are able to feed on atmospheric nitrogen, releasing it ultimately in the soil as simple chemicals such as nitrates. Billions of these bacteria inhabit the top few inches of most soils, working independently at their job of ' fixing ' nitrogen. But there are others that live in association with leguminous plants like peas and beans, lupins and clover. As the plants grow they are invaded by bacteria which form colonies inside little nodules on the plant's roots. Inside these nodules the bacteria set up house and establish a happy relationship with the plant they have selected as their host. In return for sugary materials provided by the plant the root bacteria feed on atmospheric nitrogen in the soil and turn it into chemical substances. This 'fixed' nitrogen is made available to the plant as payment for the sugars it has given to the bacteria. It is an arrangement that works to the mutual benefit of both parties.

It is this ability to draw supplies of nitrogen from the air that enables leguminous plants to enrich the soil in which they grow. These plants replenish the supplies of nitrogen chemicals in the soil, instead of using them up as other plants do.

Although Nature relies so much upon bacteria to bridge the gap between atmospheric nitrogen and the nitrogen that is needed by the living world, she does not depend entirely on bacteria for supplies of fixed nitrogen. Whenever lightning flashes through the air it activates the reluctant nitrogen to the point where it will enter into chemical union with the oxygen. Oxides of nitrogen formed in the air are dissolved by rain and changed to nitrates in the soil. Although this might appear to make only a trivial contribution to the store of nitrogen chemicals in the soil, it is in fact of great importance in the cycle of nitrogen between the atmosphere and the earth. In Britain some 11lb. of fixed nitrogen are delivered annually to every acre of ground in this way. In tropical countries, where electric discharges in the air are very much more frequent, the amount is greater still.

By these two routes, with the help of bacteria and the electricity in the air, the atmosphere is able to feed the soil with a supply of nitrogen chemicals needed by the vegetation it supports. But this constant flow of nitrogen chemicals into the soil is not the main source of nitrogen to the plant. The bulk of the nitrogen chemicals are released into the soil by the decay of once-living matter; the new plant depends on second-hand nitrogen that has already been used by previous plant and animal generations. When living things die their remains are attacked by multitudes of hungry micro-organisms in the soil. Feeding on the body substances, the carbohydrates, fats, and proteins, the microbes break up the complex chemical structures of these materials into simpler substances that they can use for rebuilding to their own requirements. The nitrogen from decaying protein becomes available in due course as simple nitrates similar to those formed by electric discharge in the air and by nitrogen-fixing bacteria.

When vegetation is growing naturally on the land the bulk of the requirements of nitrogen come from plant and animal remains that fall continually on the soil. Extra supplies are brought in by the lightning discharges in the atmosphere and by nitrogen-fixing bacteria. Other bacteria are hard at work undoing what their colleagues have done; they break up the nitrates into nitrogen gas again. The growth of vegetation adjusts itself to the amount of nitrogen and other foods available in the soil.

Where man has come and imposed his agriculture on the soil he has upset the balance established by Nature. His needs are more urgent than can be met by the natural growing-power of the land. He wants the soil to return more food than it will do when left to its own devices.

When soil is cultivated intensively the demands made on it are much greater than those that are made by Nature. Much of the crop is taken away and used as food instead of returning its substance to the soil.

As he migrated into the great prairie lands of the New World man cropped the virgin ground remorse-

lessly to provide food that was needed by industrial
countries. Crop after crop was taken from the soil,
which could not restore the supplies of nitrogen and
other chemical foods.

By the end of the nineteenth century the wheat-
growing lands were becoming exhausted to the point
where the food supply of the Western World was
threatened. In particular the soil needed nitrogen in a
form that could be absorbed by the growing plant. It
needed chemical foods such as nitrates similar to those
provided by lightning and bacteria.

In the air there are vast stores of nitrogen gas. But,
as such, nitrogen is virtually useless to the plant. To be
of value as a plant food it must be united with other
elements in the form of chemicals that can be dissolved
in the water of the soil. The development of methods
of making these chemicals in vast quantities from
atmosphere nitrogen has been one of the great chemical
achievements of the century. Its effect on mankind
overshadows the influence even of atomic energy.

The successful ' fixation ' of atmosphere nitrogen was
accomplished during the early years of the twentieth
century. Following Nature's lead, scientists used the
electric discharge to unite the oxygen and nitrogen of
the air. From the nitric acid formed they made nitrates.
This process was superseded by the manufacture of
synthetic ammonia from atmospheric nitrogen and the
hydrogen of water. Ammonium sulphate, made from this
synthetic ammonia, provides bacteria in the soil with a
raw material that they can turn into nitrates. It has
become the most important of all the synthetic nitrogen-
containing fertilizers.

To-day the manufacture of ammonium sulphate and
other nitrogenous fertilizers is one of the world's great
industries. More than two million tons of fertilizers are
made every year from atmospheric nitrogen. Without

these plant-food chemicals we should be unable to provide the food needed by the expanding population of the world.

Agriculture, however, is only one of the outlets for nitrogen chemicals in the modern world. Nitrogen captured from the air is needed for all manner of synthetic substances. Every day the versatility of nitrogen increases, and as the chemical industry pours out its array of new materials, so does the demand for nitrogen chemicals become more pressing.

Nitrogen is a constituent of most of the high explosives that do so much of the donkey work in mining and quarrying. Nitrogen is reluctant to join forces with other elements; once it has done so it is often anxious to release itself from its chemical bondage. Many modern explosives are chemicals containing carbon and hydrogen, together with the oxygen they need to turn themselves instantaneously into gas. Nitrogen is united with these elements, providing the source of chemical temperament that enables the internal 'burning' to take place.

In 1846 Schönbein, a Swiss chemistry professor, found that the harmless cellulose of cotton, containing only carbon, hydrogen, and oxygen, could be made into nitro-cellulose when treated with nitric acid. Under a suitable stimulus this 'gun cotton' will explode, its carbon and hydrogen burning instantaneously in the oxygen that is united with them in the nitro-cellulose. The nitrogen liberates itself once more into the air.

Other carbon- and hydrogen-containing substances can be turned into explosives with the help of nitrogen. Glycerine becomes nitro-glycerine; soaked into an inert material, such as the porous earth called kieselguhr, it forms dynamite.

Though the discovery of nitro-cellulose opened the way to modern high explosives, it was the beginning of other industries as well. Nitro-cellulose will dissolve in solvents such as alcohol and ether; spread on to a surface these solutions will dry and leave a thin film of nitro-cellulose. This is the basis of the synthetic lacquer industry, which uses immense amounts of cellulose from wood and nitric acid from atmospheric nitrogen. Spread on to a fabric backing, solutions of nitro-cellulose provide us with much of our leather-cloth.

In 1865 Alexander Parkes, a Birmingham metallurgist, described how nitro-cellulose could be dissolved in warm camphor, forming a plastic mass that hardened as it cooled to a tough, flexible material. This was celluloid, the first synthetic plastic. The vast synthetic plastics industry had begun with the help of nitrogen. And nitrogen is still a constituent of many plastics to-day.

In 1883 Sir Joseph Swan patented a process for squirting nitro-cellulose solutions through holes to form filaments which hardened in the air as the solvent evaporated. These were among the first of the rayon fibres, which have become the basis of a tremendous modern industry.

When the development of nylon was announced in 1938 it heralded another step forward in the textile industry. Made entirely from simple chemicals, nylon was the first commercially successful synthetic fibre. One of its constituents is nitrogen, taken originally from the air.

Nitrogen goes into hundreds of the synthetic substances that have become so much a part of modern life. It helps to provide us with our paints and dyestuffs, vitamins and hormones, synthetic drugs and disinfectants. It goes into synthetic rubbers, and into insecticides, and agricultural chemicals.

One of the most exciting of all the developments in nitrogen chemistry has been in protein research. The proteins, which play such a fundamental role in life, are amongst the most complex of all chemical substances. The atoms of carbon, hydrogen, oxygen, nitrogen, and other elements are arranged into bewildering patterns inside the protein molecules. Many proteins have thousands of atoms joined together in their molecules; some have a million or more. Tracing out the structure of a protein molecule is a heart-breaking task for the chemist; fitting atoms together in an attempt to synthesize a protein is a seemingly impossible project. Yet a start has been made.

In 1947 a young American chemist, Robert Woodward, made a synthetic protein-like material in the laboratory. The significance of this great step in synthetic nitrogen chemistry has yet to be appreciated to the full.

The enzymes that control our bodies are mainly protein in their structure. What could be the effect of making such substances in the laboratory?

The protoplasm in every living cell is partly protein; synthesis of protein could take us towards a solution of the mystery of the life-force itself.

Viruses, the strange disease - producing microorganisms that lie midway between the inanimate chemical and the living thing, are proteins. Some day it may be possible to make synthetic viruses similar to those that are the cause of 'flu or poliomyelitis. If so we could perhaps make modifications of their chemical structure that would render them harmless; yet they would be sufficiently like the disease-producing viruses to stimulate the defences of the body against their deadly relatives.

Some of the antibiotic drugs are proteins. We may be able to manufacture them synthetically from nitrogen that is taken from the air.

At present the prospect of being able to make our proteins in the laboratory is incredibly remote. We have made a start, but it could be fifty years or a hundred before we can duplicate the detailed chemical structure of a natural protein. We are a long way yet from being able to assure ourselves of a supply of synthetic meat or milk, of synthetic fish or eggs made in the chemical factory from atmospheric nitrogen.

It could well be, however, that we shall have no need to make synthetic proteins for use as human food. Although we build our body proteins from those that are provided ready-made in our food, we break the food proteins into simpler chemicals as they are being digested. These simple protein constituents, amino acids, are absorbed into the bloodstream and used as building-blocks by the tissues; from them the living cells recreate the proteins they require. Instead of providing proteins in our food, we can supply the proteins pre-digested in the form of amino acids. And amino acids are comparatively simple to make synthetically from nitrogen and other chemicals.

Although the living world makes use of thousands of different varieties of protein, they are all constructed from only twenty-three different amino acids. The simplest of these has ten atoms joined together in the molecule; the most complex has only thirty-five. Yet by the joining together of these small amino acid molecules the body can build proteins with millions of atoms attached to one another in incredibly complex structures. Egg albumin, one of the simpler proteins, has about 300 amino acids joined together in its molecule; some of the proteins of the human body have 30,000 or more.

When proteins are digested their massive molecules are split into the constituent amino acids; no matter how complex the protein may have been it yields no more than twenty-three different amino acid units.

These amino acids are like the letters of the alphabet.

They can be joined together to form innumerable different words, or combinations containing any number of letters arranged in any order. There is no limit to the complexity that may result from only twenty-six letters of the alphabet. Each combination of letters corresponds to a different protein structure.

Not all the amino acids are used in every protein. Some proteins contain many of the twenty-three amino acids, some have few. Linked together the acids form a chain-like molecule in which each amino acid is a link. The arrangement of the amino acid links relative to one another and the proportion of each one present in the molecule determines the nature of the protein itself.

During the last twenty years biochemists have learned much about the amino acids needed in animal and human diets. Many food proteins have been analysed and their amino acid content found. The amount of each amino acid needed to sustain the body has been determined. And it has been shown that we can make these amino acids do duty for the protein that we normally prefer to eat. All the amino acids can be made synthetically; some are already being manufactured on an impressive scale.

Although the body needs the twenty-three different amino acids in order to build its vast array of proteins, it can provide some of them for itself if they are lacking in the food protein. Only eight of the twenty-three must be present as such in the diet; the rest can be manufactured by the body from other proteins and foods. The eight 'essential' amino acids, however, cannot be built by the body itself; they must be present ready-made in the proteins of the food. If they are not the tissues cannot build some of the proteins that they need. And the body suffers.

In countries where living standards are high and food

is rich in proteins of different types there is sufficient of every one of the eight essential amino acids in the diet. But in some of the under-privileged parts of the world —in Africa and South-East Asia, in Central and South America—the diet is often monotonous and lacks a proper supply of mixed proteins. Milk, eggs, and butter are major sources of proteins containing the essential amino acids; but there are millions of people in the world who see little of these foods in their daily diet. Often the source of protein is restricted to one or two staple vegetable foods; manioc, for example, is the basic food in many parts of Africa, and rice in South-East Asia. With such diets people may have insufficient of one or more essential amino acids in their food. In particular four amino acids are often lacking in low-quality protein diets. These are methionine, lysine, tryptophane, and threonine.

Where these amino acids are in short supply the tissues cannot provide the proteins needed for body-growth. Children do not grow as quickly as they should, nor do they reach their proper stature. They are undeveloped, with poor muscle structures. Adults, as well as children, become anæmic and are unable to resist the attack of disease.

In the Congo districts of Africa babies grow well during their first three months of life. But as they are weaned from their mothers' milk and begin to depend on the largely vegetable diet of the community their growth-rate slows. They are getting plenty of protein in their diet, but there is little variety in it. One or more of the essential amino acids is lacking, and the body cannot build the proteins that it needs.

The difficulties of making good these deficiencies are increased by the body's inability to store its proteins. Fats and carbohydrates can be stored to some extent in the body tissues. But proteins must be given regularly in the diet, and a proper ration of the essential amino acids should reach the tissues every day.

Although it has been shown that amino acids can substitute entirely for natural proteins in human food, there is little prospect of a dose of amino acids doing duty for the week-end joint. But there is an immediate and urgent job for amino acids to do in supplementing the low-quality protein diets that lack one or other of the essential acids. Small additions of these acids can change a poor diet into an adequate one.

Used in this way, essential amino acids will not only fortify low-quality protein food but will release great quantities of much-needed protein to the world. In the absence of essential amino acids in the diet many of the other amino acids derived from the proteins are wasted. Without supplies of the essential amino acids the body cannot construct the proteins it needs; much of the protein in the food becomes useless.

A great deal of experimental work has been carried out on the assessment of amino acid fortification of basic foods. Its results may prove to be of the greatest benefit to mankind. It has been found, for example, that additions of the amino acid lysine to bread can double the value of the bread as a tissue builder. This is like adding an egg a day to the average diet. It has been estimated that by making use of present knowledge on amino acid fortification we could double the supply of useful protein food that is available to the world.

Already amino acids are being widely used in medicine; they can provide the body with raw materials for tissue-building when food proteins are unsuitable. After operations affecting the digestive organs, for example, the body needs amino acids for repairing the damaged tissue, but it cannot obtain them from food protein. People who have been badly burned need great quantities of protein. Sometimes they could use as much

as three pounds of meat a day to provide the raw
material for building new tissue. Yet it is impossible for
a patient suffering from severe shock to digest any
appreciable amount of protein at all. Amino acids can
be given instead; if necessary they are injected directly
into the bloodstream.

During the great Bengal famine of 1943 amino acids
were used for the first time on a major scale to make
good the lack of food protein. After the war pre-digested
proteins in the form of amino acids were given to
starving people who were desperately in need of body-
building raw material. Unable to digest the proteins
that they had done without for months or even years
they depended on amino acids to tide them over until
their bodies were restored to health.

In their chemical structure all the amino acids bear a
family resemblance to the simple chemical ammonia,
which is manufactured in vast quantities from the
nitrogen of the air. Much of this synthetic ammonia is
made into fertilizers that are used as food for growing
crops. The nitrogen imprisoned in these chemicals is,
in fact, the nitrogen that is built into proteins by the
plant. It is the nitrogen that is in the amino acids
formed when our food protein is digested. By making
amino acids synthetically from ammonia we are short-
circuiting the route from atmospheric nitrogen to the
nitrogen-containing raw materials needed by our living
tissues.

8

Carbon Dioxide feeds the World

WHEREVER living things are breathing air to provide themselves with oxygen they are exhaling a corresponding amount of carbon dioxide gas. This gas, formed by the union of carbon and oxygen, is discarded by living things; it is a waste-product formed from organic substances which have released their stored-up energy by 'burning' in the oxygen of the air.

Bacteria liberate carbon dioxide as they feed upon decaying matter in the soil. Yeasts, moulds, and other micro-organisms discard carbon dioxide which is often made to do a useful job of work. Yeasts feed on sugary materials in warm dough, liberating carbon dioxide that makes the bread porous by filling it with holes. In beer the flourishing yeasts provide the carbon dioxide that gives the beer its head. Insects and animals exhale carbon dioxide that has come from the carbon in their food. Plants lose carbon dioxide when the sugar made in their leaves is burned as fuel in the growing tissues.

From all these living things, and from all the fires and furnaces, the cars and ships and planes, that are burning fuel, a silent, invisible stream of carbon dioxide gas is flowing steadily into the atmosphere. In city streets and crowded trains and offices the air receives an overdose of carbon dioxide that raises its concentration above the normal level. But soon the wind is churning the air until these local concentrations disappear and are lost in the lofty ocean of the atmosphere.

The amount of carbon dioxide in the air remains constant over most of the surface of the earth. One part of carbon dioxide is mixed with about 3000 parts of air. Altogether there are 680,000 million tons of it in the atmosphere. In the water that covers two-thirds of the earth's surface there is an even larger reservoir of carbon dioxide; 22 million million tons of it are dissolved in the seas and lakes of the world.

Like other constituents of the air—oxygen, nitrogen, and water vapour—the carbon dioxide is part of an unceasing cycle of interchange between the atmosphere and the living things that inhabit the earth. From atmospheric carbon dioxide comes all the carbon that forms the bulk of every plant and animal.

The plants that blanket the surface of the earth and float in large quantities on the sea depend on carbon dioxide as their staple food. Air circulating through the leaves of land plants is stripped of its carbon dioxide by the spongy cells inside the leaves. The outer surfaces of these cells are covered with a moisture film; the carbon dioxide dissolves in the water and is absorbed into the interior of the cells. From this carbon dioxide and from water absorbed through the roots the chlorophyll in the green cells creates the complex substances that sustain the living tissues of the plant. Sugars are made from carbon dioxide and water in the leaves; distributed about the plant, they supply the active cells with raw material and provide them with a source of energy.

During the manufacture of sugar in the leaves the carbon dioxide and water between them supply more oxygen than is needed for construction of the sugar. The extra oxygen is liberated into the leaves and flows out with air. Energy drawn from the sunshine to bring about the chemical change is stored as chemical energy inside the sugar.

This process of photosynthesis, which draws upon the supplies of carbon dioxide in the air, is the reverse of respiration. It makes good the losses of carbon from living things that are forever burning up their body materials to provide themselves with energy.

In human respiration carbon dioxide is formed within the living tissues; carbon-containing substances are burning in the oxygen carried to them by the blood. Carbon dioxide dissolves in the blood and is brought back to the lungs, where it escapes into the air. Exhaled air contains about 4 per cent. of carbon dioxide, compared with the 0.03 per cent. in the air that is breathed in.

Although this carbon dioxide in the breath is simply a waste material, it nevertheless fulfils a vital function in the body. The concentration of carbon dioxide in the blood affects the breathing rate: if there is too much carbon dioxide it stimulates the rate and depth of breathing. The lungs are given more air and the carbon dioxide is cleared away more rapidly. In medicine carbon dioxide is often used deliberately to stimulate the breathing of a patient. Five per cent. of carbon dioxide in the air is sufficient to cause panting and to increase the pulse-rate.

Carbon dioxide is used for treating nervous diseases. Courses of carbon dioxide inhalations have brought remarkable cures in cases of stammering, anxiety, alcoholism, and other neuroses. The gas is believed to dull the sensitivity of nerve cells, making them less easily stimulated. It helps to provide a barrier to the indiscriminate stimulation of brain cells that can cause harmful neuroses.

For many years the design of ventilation systems has been based on the assumption that carbon dioxide in the air should not exceed 0.1 per cent. It is now known that this concentration is quite innocuous, and carbon dioxide is not regarded as being unduly poisonous. People can safely breathe air containing 5 per cent. or more without coming to any harm. Carbon dioxide becomes noxious only when it is breathed continually at a concentration of 10 per cent. or more.

Like other gases of the air, carbon dioxide has become an industrial raw material of great importance. Compressed into steel cylinders, it is stored and distributed as a liquid. When the valve of the cylinder is opened the liquid evaporates and carbon dioxide gas streams from the cylinder. But as it expands into the comparatively low pressure of the atmosphere the gas cools. Some of it turns to solid carbon dioxide which forms little particles in the gas stream.

Used in this way carbon dioxide is an effective fire-fighting agent. As the gas is heavier than the air, it lies like a blanket over burning substances. It is inert and cuts off the supply of air that is essential when anything burns. Denied its oxygen, the fire dies away.

The little particles of solid carbon dioxide in the escaping gas stream are at a temperature of about $-110°F$. They cool the material that is burning and damp the ardour of the chemical reaction between it and the oxygen of the air.

Solid carbon dioxide is becoming an invaluable cold-storage material. In well-insulated containers it evaporates so slowly that it can be stored and distributed without difficulty. As it evaporates it disappears into the air as carbon dioxide gas; 'dry ice' is therefore a clean and convenient material for cooling ice-cream and frozen-food containers.

When modern machines are being built it is often difficult to fit the parts together. Solid carbon dioxide is used to cool machined parts, so that they shrink and can be easily assembled. As they warm up again they are restored to their normal size, giving an accurate fit.

Wherever our modern life-saving gadgets have to be blown up quickly and automatically carbon dioxide does the job. It fills everything from life-jackets and rubber dinghies to motor tyres and bridge pontoons.

Although the air contains unlimited supplies of carbon dioxide, the concentration is too low to make its extraction worthwhile. Much of the carbon dioxide needed for industrial use is manufactured as a by-product by the synthetic fertilizer industry. Synthetic ammonia is made by chemical union between nitrogen and hydrogen. The air is the source of nitrogen, and the hydrogen comes from water; in each case the gases needed are contaminated with unwanted oxygen. The nitrogen is mixed with oxygen in the air, and the hydrogen is combined chemically with it in water. Oxygen is removed by passing air and steam over red-hot coke. The coke burns in the oxygen contained in both the air and the water, forming carbon dioxide which can easily be separated from the gas stream. Nitrogen and hydrogen are left and are ultimately joined together to form ammonia. The carbon dioxide, which was originally an almost worthless by-product, has become a valuable material in its own right.

Although the carbon dioxide in the atmosphere remains at a concentration of 0.03 per cent. all over the world, the amount in the air has not always been the same. There have been periods in the world's history when the air became charged with more carbon dioxide than it now carries; there have also been periods when the concentration has fallen unusually low.

The effects of these changes have been profound. They are believed to have influenced the climate of the earth by controlling the amount of energy that is lost by the earth into space. Nearly a century ago the British scientist John Tyndall suggested that a fall in the atmospheric carbon dioxide could allow the earth to cool, whereas a rise in carbon dioxide would make it warmer.

With the help of its carbon dioxide the atmosphere acts like a greenhouse that traps the heat of the sun. Radiations reaching the atmosphere as sunshine can penetrate to the surface of the earth; here they are absorbed, providing the world with warmth. But the earth itself is radiating energy outwards in the form of long-wave heat rays. If these could penetrate the air as the sunshine does they would carry off much of the heat provided by the sun. Carbon dioxide in the air helps to stop the escape of heat radiations. It acts like a blanket that keeps the world warm. And the more carbon dioxide the air contains, the more efficiently does it smother the escape of the earth's heat.

Fluctuation in the carbon dioxide of the air has helped to bring about major climate changes experienced by the world in the past. During the hundreds of millions of years that the earth has existed its temperature has been rising and falling over long periods of time. As the earth became warmer huge forests of tropical vegetation covered the land; when the temperature fell the ice flowed down from the poles and the frozen ground was held in the grip of another Ice Age.

For most of its life the world has been warmer than it is now. Only for relatively short periods of time, measured by as little as a million years, have the ice sheets covered the earth.

At present we are recovering from an Ice Age that reached its climax about twenty thousand years ago. Europe was covered with ice as far south as the Mediterranean; ice lay over Canada and much of the United States and reached down into Asia. Now the ice has retreated and the glaciers in the mountains are melting as the world warms up again. During the last century the climate of the world has become hotter by about 2°F. In some northern countries the average winter temperature has risen by 15°F or more in the last forty years.

Although this rise in temperature does not seem very large, it is of the very greatest importance in its effect on the immediate future of the world. If the warming-up continues at its present rate another fifty years will see so much ice melted from the polar ice caps that the sea will be encroaching on some of our low-lying coasts. A drop in temperature of a few degrees, on the other hand, could bring the ice back to northern countries that have been free of it for thousands of years.

Nobody knows what is bringing about these fluctuations in the temperature of the earth. But it seems certain that the carbon dioxide content of the air is one of the causes. Many factors are influencing the amount of carbon dioxide that is liberated into the air and the amount that is taken from it. Over long periods of time changes in the balance of give and take could raise or lower the concentrations of carbon dioxide in the air.

Vegetation absorbs thousands of millions of tons of carbon dioxide every year as raw material for making its living matter. Ideally this carbon dioxide is all returned to the air as the dead material decays. But in days gone by vast layers of dead organic matter have been trapped and buried, forming coal and oil that now supply us with so much of our power. These deposits of coal and oil represent billions of tons of carbon dioxide stripped from the air.

Much of the corrosion and weathering of the rocks in the earth's surface is caused by carbon dioxide from the air. Dissolved in water, carbon dioxide forms a weak acid that eats away steadily at the exposed surface of the rocks. Every year more than 100 million tons of carbon dioxide are used up in this large-scale etching of the land. But in the past, when the earth was settling its surface into place, the carbon dioxide was given even greater opportunities. Where upheavals in the earth's crust have taken place fresh rock surfaces have been exposed and the carbon dioxide of the air has had every chance of eating away the rock. Geological evidence has shown that the creation of some of the world's most impressive mountain ranges has been followed by encroachment of the polar ice. By denuding the atmosphere of its carbon dioxide the fresh rock surfaces thrust into the air have encouraged more radiant heat to escape from the earth into space. The temperature of the earth has fallen, and the ice has come.

As the land settled into place and the carbon dioxide built up its concentration in the air again vegetation once more replaced the melting ice. Feeding on the abundant carbon dioxide, plants took over the earth and covered it with tropical vegetation. Even Antarctica supported huge plants and trees, of which the remains have been found in coal seams under the ice.

The carbon dioxide absorbed by these plants that flourished many millions of years ago is now helping the world to recover from its most recent ice age. Pouring from millions of chimneys all over the world, carbon dioxide from coal and oil is helping the atmosphere to hold the world's heat.

As the plants died their remains were covered over and trapped by layers of earth and rock. The carbon-containing substances of the plants, which had found their origin in the carbon dioxide of the air, were squeezed and heated until they turned into coal. Coal is a store of carbon chemicals left for us by the atmosphere that covered the earth millions of years ago. Oil, formed from the remains of countless creatures of the sea, contains carbon chemicals different from those we derive from coal. But they came, no less, from carbon dioxide in the air of prehistoric times.

During the last two hundred years industrialization of the world has been possible only by plundering its reserves of stored fuel on a prodigious scale. Mountains of coal and oceans of oil have been burned in fires and furnaces, trains and cars and ships all over the world. The carbon that was stored away in them has poured into the atmosphere from which it was taken before man appeared on earth.

From every ton of coal that is burned two and a half tons of carbon dioxide are released into the air. Altogether six billion tons of carbon dioxide are being produced from fuel every year. This stream of gas is so immense that it is increasing the amount of carbon dioxide held permanently in the air. Measurements have shown that since 1900 the carbon dioxide content of the air has increased by a tenth. This alone is sufficient to account for the increasing temperature of the world.

The effect of our extra carbon dioxide does not stop at warming up our climate. Radiation from the tops of clouds is cut down as the amount of carbon dioxide in the air increases. The difference in temperature between the top and bottom of the cloud is lowered, and the convection currents are more gentle. The effect of this is to discourage clouds from turning to rain.

Although there is a lot to be said for trapping the dirt and chemicals that are poured into the air from domestic fires and industrial furnaces, there would seem to be every reason for producing as much carbon dioxide as we can manage. It is helping us towards a warmer and drier world.

9

Water in the Air

Two-thirds of the surface of the earth is covered by water. In the lakes and seas there are three hundred million cubic miles of water; billions of tons of water vapour float in the air above the earth. Upon this enormous ration of water the entire life of the world depends.

Between the air and the seas there flows a constant interchange of liquid water and water vapour. The water of the sea is rich in salts. For millions of years the rainwater trickling over the surface of the earth has eaten away the rocks and minerals, dissolving the soluble substances and carrying them down to the sea. Seawater is now a solution of hundreds of different minerals; it is useless as a source of water for domestic or industrial purposes. We depend on the air to purify it for us.

Oxygen, nitrogen, and most of the other gases of the air are mixed together in proportions that remain virtually constant over the entire surface of the earth. But the amount of water vapour varies continually from place to place and from day to day. Like other gases in the air, water vapour is invisible. Only when the water appears in liquid form does it become visible; a cloud is not water vapour—it is liquid water floating in the air in the form of tiny droplets.

When air is warm it can absorb more water vapour than it does when cold. Warm air that is saturated with water vapour will therefore dispense with some of it as liquid water if it is cooled. The water collects on dust particles in the air, forming droplets that become visible as a cloud. These droplets are so small that 100 billions would not fill a teacup. Yet they are the substance of all the clouds in the sky, from the flimsy curtains of cirrus to the towering masses of cumulonimbus that carry their threat of thunder and rain.

As it wafts over the sea and the wet surface of the land air takes up supplies of water in the form of invisible water vapour. The salts of the sea-water are left behind, and the water carried off by the air is pure. Caught up in the general turmoil of the atmosphere, the air may be swept aloft. As it rises it cools; it can no longer hold so much water vapour, and the droplets of liquid water appear. Beneath each cloud in a summer sky is an invisible column of warm, wet air that carries its cloud like a cotton wool crown.

Left to themselves the tiny droplets in the cloud are too small to fall to the ground. They float away, perhaps to be turned to water vapour again as the air is warmed. But if the droplets can collect together they become heavy enough to fall, and will reach the earth as rain or hail or snow.

As it reaches the ground rainwater contains none of the salts that were dissolved in it in the sea. During its journey through the air it dissolves small quantities of air-borne gases and chemicals. But compared with sea-water it is pure. Distilled by the air, it flows into our lakes and reservoirs.

Vast oceans of water are carried by the air in this interchange of moisture between the earth and its atmosphere. Vapour in the air above every square mile of the earth's surface would fill a reservoir with nearly two and a half million cubic feet of water. Without this water the desiccated air would be filled with chok-

ing dust and dirt. The air would not be able to play its
part in modifying the extremes of climate in different
parts of the world. Heat would escape from the earth,
and the land would be gripped by arctic frosts. Only a
sixth of the radiations leaving the earth are allowed to
escape into space; the rest are absorbed largely by the
carbon dioxide and water vapour in the air.

Most of the release of liquid water by the air takes
place high up in the atmosphere, and clouds are formed.
But air that is saturated with water vapour can also be
cooled at ground level. Billions of tiny water droplets
appear in the air, and the result is fog. Fog is a low-level
cloud.

Though clouds have a tremendous effect on human
life in many ways, they do not influence our activities
so directly as does fog. In war fog has changed the
course of history. For his last great offensive in the West
Hitler made use of an impenetrable blanket of fog. It
covered his Ardennes push, protecting the German
armies from the overwhelming air power of the Allied
Nations. This was not the first time that fog had played
a major role in military operations. Napoleon escaped
from Egypt under the cover of Mediterranean fog. Fog
stilled the battle between a million men at Loos in May
1917, overruling the orders of the High Commands.

In times of peace fog is a factor to be reckoned with
in our everyday affairs. Without warning it will settle
over sea and land, crippling the work of our great ports
and airfields and bringing the activities of millions of
people in our cities to a standstill.

Britain has more than its fair share of fogs. Summer
and winter there is usually fog in one place or another.
But there are foggier places on earth. Worst of the lot
is the area of the Grand Banks near Newfoundland,
where fog is the rule rather than the exception.

In Britain and along the north-west seaboard of

Europe conditions favour fog production. The prevailing winds are westerly. By the time they reach Europe they have blown across the path of Atlantic water warmed by the Gulf Stream. They arrive over the land laden with moisture and all too anxious to get rid of some of it. The only encouragement they need is to be cooled.

In winter the land loses heat more rapidly than the sunshine can replace it, and it becomes cold. As the winds blow in from the Atlantic they are cooled by contact with the ground itself. The water vapour turns into water droplets that float around near the surface of the earth. The result is fog. This type of fog, caused by direct contact between moisture-laden air and the cold surface of the earth, is called advection fog. It is commonest during autumn and winter when the land is cold in comparison with the sea. Advection fogs are also the fogs which plague our ships at sea when warm moist air is blowing over a cold current. In spring and summer, for example, warm air blowing from the land can release fog when it comes in contact with the cold surface of the sea. This is the type of fog that blankets the Grand Banks and the Newfoundland coast.

A second type of fog is caused by radiation. On cloudless nights heat radiates rapidly away from the earth into the atmosphere. As the earth cools it cools the air in contact with it; if the air is sufficiently soaked with moisture it begins to lose some of it as liquid water.

If there is a light wind blowing the cooled air is stirred up and mixed so that a thick layer of cold air is formed above the earth's surface. The moisture will be released from the cooling air in the form of tiny droplets; the result, again, is fog. For radiation fog to appear conditions must be just right. If the wind is too boisterous the water droplets will be dispersed, and fog will not be able to form. If, on the other hand, the air is quite still water will be deposited from the air in contact with the ground, forming dew.

The long nights of autumn and winter favour radiation fog, as the earth has more opportunity to cool. The fog will tend to form in valleys with cold air rolling down from the hillsides. Radiation fogs are often at their worst in the early hours of the morning when the first rays of the sun cause turbulence in the air near the earth's surface, mixing it and creating a layer of fog. If conditions are suitable these fogs will persist for days on end. As water does not cool by radiation so rapidly as the land, radiation fogs do not appear at sea.

In common with the high-level cloud a fog needs nuclei in the air to enable it to form. Water droplets will build up around particles of solid material, and the number of these particles in the air plays a big part in controlling fog formation.

Over the sea little particles of salt from sea spray can act as fog nuclei. Over the land there are always dust particles even in the air of the countryside. But it is in our industrial areas that we really make sure that fog has every opportunity to form. Billions of particles of soot and smoke are poured into the air every day, providing ideal nuclei around which fog droplets can grow. In place of the relatively harmless sea fog or the haze of the countryside we get the acrid, dangerous smoke fogs which have become such a menace to us to-day.

As meteorology has developed its scientific status in recent years the water of the air has claimed a new branch of the science to itself. Research in this specialized field of cloud physics has made rapid progress, and much has been learned of the processes involved in rain production. It is a complex phenomenon.

The gathering together of tiny droplets in a cloud is believed to take place when some of the droplets freeze to form ice crystals. The rest of the water droplets collect on to these ice nuclei and build up into snow-flakes that become heavy enough to begin falling through the air. As like as not thè flakes will pass through warmer air on their way to the ground and turn to rain. If they remain frozen they will land as snow. If they melt and freeze again by passing through a belt of cold air they may reach the ground as hail.

Although this process sounds simple enough, it represents only one of several possible ways in which rain is formed. There are many factors involved in the process, about which we know very little. Changes from one form of ice crystal to another, for example, may play a part in rain production.

British physicists have made a study of the various shapes of crystal that reach the ground as snow. The shapes are preserved by allowing snow-flakes to fall into a special syrupy plastic. As the syrup is kept below the freezing point of water, a snow-flake falling on it does not melt. The plastic is then allowed to harden with the snow-flake embedded in it. After the plastic has set the snow-flake is allowed to melt, and the water from it is absorbed into the plastic. It leaves behind a hollow in the plastic that is the exact shape of the original crystals forming the snow-flake.

Most astonishing of all the achievements in cloud physics has been the successful development of weather control. Clouds have been persuaded to turn themselves into snow and rain; water has been brought to areas suffering from drought. Since 1946 American scientists have led the way in this aspect of cloud physics. On November 13, of that year, a young American scientist, Dr Vincent Schaefer, made the first artificial snowstorm in history. It was the culmination of experiments carried out during the war by Schaefer and Irving Langmuir, a Nobel prizewinner of 1932. These scientists were studying ice formation on aircraft. Their investigations took them to the summit of Mount Washington, in New Hampshire, where they could find the sort of conditions that built up the ice on an aircraft's wings.

During their stay on Mount Washington the scientists were surprised to find that many of the clouds surrounding them were supercooled. That is to say, the billions of tiny droplets that formed the cloud were actually colder than the temperature at which water normally freezes. And yet the droplets remained as liquid water instead of turning into ice.

These supercooled water droplets were in a very sensitive state. Given the slightest encouragement they would start freezing suddenly and collect together as snowflakes big enough to fall to the ground.

When he returned to his laboratory Schaefer began experimenting to find out more about these supercooled clouds. He made miniature clouds by breathing into a refrigerator. And he found that there was a certain temperature (– 38°F.) below which the water droplets had to turn to ice. Above this temperature they could stay as liquid even though below their normal freezing point and form a supercooled cloud.

Schaefer then found that in a supercooled cloud it was necessary to persuade only a few droplets to freeze in order to start the whole cloud freezing. A metal rod chilled to below – 38°F. and waved in a laboratory cloud would turn the entire cloud into snow. The rod was cold enough to force a few droplets to freeze. And once this happened the rest of the droplets froze too.

What Schaefer had discovered, therefore, was a way of turning supercooled clouds into snowflakes heavy enough to fall. He had done it in the laboratory. But could he do the same thing with a full-sized cloud? On November 13, 1946, Schaefer put his discovery to the test. He went up in a plane near Schenectady and

A CLOUD AT GROUND-LEVEL
December in London.

Photo J. K. A. Bleasdale, B.Sc., Ph.D., (National Smoke Abatement Society)

AIR POLLUTION AND PLANT GROWTH

These typical plants of Aberystwyth S23 rye-grass were grown in plots of standard soil receiving different levels of atmospheric pollution. Planted November 1, 1950; photographed April 19, 1951. (1) Pure air; (2) suburban air; (3) Manchester air (near centre of city).

Photo National Smoke Abatement Society

A LION DISSOLVED

The effects of acid-laden air in London.

found a supercooled cloud at 14,000 feet. Schaefer believed that if he could cool a few of the droplets in the cloud sufficiently to turn them to ice he would turn the entire cloud into snowflakes. To provide the sudden chilling of the droplets Schaefer had brought with him some solid carbon dioxide, or 'dry ice,' which has a temperature of $-110°F$. He scattered six pounds of his 'dry ice' into the cloud; the four-mile-long cloud turned into a snowstorm that fell 2000 feet before evaporating.

At this stage Schaefer and his fellow weather scientists realized that experiments like this could make them unpopular. Snow in large quantities, deposited where it was not welcome, could result in heavy claims for damages. It was decided that responsibility for further large-scale experiments should be handed over to the United States Signal Corps.

Once Schaefer had shown that it was possible to produce artificial snow, scientists began trying to find other ways of stimulating supercooled clouds. One of Schaefer's colleagues, Bernard Vonnegut, suggested that the supercooled water droplets might be persuaded to turn to ice if crystals resembling ice were scattered into the cloud. Silver iodide crystals were tried; they are similar in shape to crystals of ice. As Vonnegut had predicted, the droplets froze around the silver iodide crystals, forming snowflakes.

The success of the early cloud-physics work in America has fired the imagination of scientists all over the world. It appeared probable that much of our rain might be coming from supercooled clouds triggered by some natural mechanism. The snowflakes formed in the cloud would melt to raindrops as they passed through warm air on the way to the ground.

In Australia scientists of the Radio-Physics Division of the Council for Scientific and Industrial Research obtained spectacular results during 1947. On February

5, of that year, a thick layer of cumulus cloud near Sydney was 'seeded' with dry ice. Five minutes later rain echoes were picked up from inside the cloud by radar. More dry ice was added and the echoes grew in intensity. Then, twenty minutes after the beginning of the experiment, heavy rain began to fall from the bottom of the cloud. When the plane landed an hour later a pillar of rain covering nearly twenty square miles was reaching the ground.

In 1949, during an unusually severe drought, experiments on cloud-seeding with dry ice were carried out in Britain. On August 3 'Operation Witchdoctor' began when scientists co-operated with the R.A.F. to try and break the drought over Teeside. As soon as suitable clouds had been reported by the Air Ministry supplies of 'dry ice' were rushed to the R.A.F. aerodrome at Middleton St George. The 'dry ice' was loaded into a home-made container built from old petrol drums. It held 200 lb. of the extra-cold solid, and its outlet fitted the camera hatch of the Wellington bomber that was used.

A suitable cloud was sighted at 10,000 feet west of the Pennines. The plane flew over it and dropped its pellets of 'dry ice.' Then it flew beneath the cloud in time to meet a heavy shower of rain heading down towards the Tees Valley Water Board Catchment area.

Five days later a second attempt was made. A larger 'dry ice' container had been built, holding 300 lb. The enemy this time was a cumulus cloud heading in over Penrith. It was 10,000 feet up and nicely sited to drop its rain in the catchment area.

At three minutes past five in the evening the cloud was bombed. Eight minutes later the top of the cloud had grown some 500 feet. At 5.23 p.m. a rainbow appeared underneath the cloud, and a heavy shower of rain had begun to fall. It reached the ground in the

Lune Forest area, and it was estimated that half the rain from the cloud was collected by the Tees Valley Water Board.

These two rain-making experiments were successful. But a third attempt failed as the plane did not catch the cloud in time. Whether the amount of water formed had any significant effect on breaking the drought is a moot point.

Although rain production offers an immediate return from experiments with cloud seeding, the possibilities of affecting weather in other ways cannot be ruled out. It has been calculated that a single dry ice pellet falling through a cloud two-thirds of a mile in thickness could produce a hundred thousand tons of snow. The heat evolved by this amount of water in the cloud being turned to snow would be roughly the same as that liberated by an atom bomb—enough to warm up a large volume of air. There is a possibility, therefore, that cloud manipulation could influence air temperature and movement; it could affect the course of hurricanes and storms. Seeding may be of great help in the tropics as a way of minimizing the damage caused by hail. Often hailstones as big as oranges will bombard the inhabitants of tropical countries. Cloud seeding could be used to increase the number of nuclei in the cloud producing the hail, so making a lot of little hailstones take the place of relatively large ones.

As often happens in scientific experiments some of the results have been unexpected. It was found, for example, that by overdoing the seeding of a cloud—by using too much dry ice—the water in the cloud could actually be prevented from turning into snow or rain. Too many ice nuclei are formed, and there is insufficient water in the cloud to build them all into flakes large enough to fall.

This discovery opened up an entirely new field of

research in cloud physics. If over-seeding could be carried out on a practical scale it would mean that we could persuade some of our clouds to float away without being able to turn to rain.

In America, where cloud-seeding work originated, artificial rain production was followed up with great vigour. Clouds have been assaulted daily by enthusiasts armed with dry ice and silver iodide. Rain-making has become almost a profession, but the practitioners have often been embarrassed by claims for damages from people who have been deluged with a surfeit of rain or snow.

Rain production is of particular interest to countries which are apt to suffer from severe droughts like Australia or Africa. In Britain there is unlikely to be any great demand for additional supplies of rain. But there are other aspects of weather manipulation which are of direct concern to Britain and other countries in the path of warm, wet winds. In particular there is the problem of dispersing fog.

During the war fog was removed from airfields with the help of the FIDO system. This reversed the fog-making process by warming the air. Special petrol burners were placed around the airfield. As the air warmed up it was able to absorb more moisture and the droplets of liquid water disappeared, leaving a 'hole' in the fog. This system was put to good use during the war, but for practical commercial use it is regarded as being too expensive. We are relying more and more on radar aids to bring planes safely through the fog. FIDO burns up high-grade fuel at a tremendous rate, and at one time during the war it was estimated that FIDO cost £1000 for each plane it brought home.

In the meantime other methods of fog dispersal have been tried out. Around San Francisco, where fogs are as familiar a sight as they are in Britain, fog has been cleared from airfields by sprinkling calcium chloride from low-flying planes. Calcium chloride is a chemical that can absorb moisture; it mops up water from the fog as blotting paper soaks up ink.

Ultrasonic waves have also been used against fog. These rapid vibrations of the air make the small droplets of water bump up against each other until they collect into drops large enough to settle out as rain.

Many fogs are supercooled, like the clouds that have been successfully turned into rain. By persuading a few of the water droplets to freeze we can encourage the remaining droplets to collect on the ice nuclei and ultimately settle out. Experiments carried out with ' dry ice ' have shown that supercooled fogs can be cleared in this way.

From the practical point of view the most satisfactory way of tackling the fog problem in individual countries is to stop pouring out smoke and fumes into the air. These particles give the water in the air every inducement to form into droplets. Many of the worst town fogs are smoke fogs, and cutting down atmospheric pollution will do much to stop them. Without the smoke we shall still have fogs. But they will be relatively innocuous ones and they will be fewer and less severe than we have at present.

10

Ozone and Others

HIGH in the stratosphere there floats an atmospheric layer that protects us from the most dangerous radiations of the sun. The gas that makes this layer effective is ozone, one of the rarest of all the gases of the atmosphere. Ozone is a modified form of oxygen. In ordinary oxygen the atoms move around in pairs. But in ozone they join together in threes, an association which gives ozone a personality different from that of its atmospheric relative.

In the earth's atmosphere as a whole there is so little ozone that its particles are outnumbered four million to one by particles of other gases. Most of this small amount of ozone is concentrated in the layer that lies between 12 and 30 miles above the earth. Above this layer the ozone virtually disappears at a height of 50 miles; and below 6 miles there is only an insignificant amount.

The ozone layer in the stratosphere is formed by ultra-violet rays acting on atmospheric oxygen. These rays agitate the oxygen atoms until they form threes in place of their normal pairs. The ozone itself is able to absorb more ultra-violet rays, and as a result the temperature of the ozone layer in the stratosphere is higher than the air immediately above and below.

Ozone can absorb ultra-violet rays efficiently even when it is present in quite small amounts. Altogether it removes one-twentieth of the sun's radiations, among them the dangerous short-wave rays that can do great damage to living things. Without our atmospheric shield of ozone we should be shrivelled and scorched unmercifully by the sun. Life as we know it would not be possible on earth.

In the lower levels of the atmosphere there is so little ozone in the air that scientists have had great difficulty in measuring it accurately. At many places near the earth's surface there is only one part of ozone in every hundred million parts of air. The air breathed by an average person during a year contains only an egg-cupful of ozone.

In spite of the difficulty of estimating the amount of such small quantities of ozone in the air, methods have been developed in recent years. Scientists can now measure the variations in the proportion of ozone in the air with great accuracy. And these changes are being studied as an important aspect of the general movement of gases in the atmosphere. With the help of balloons and rockets ozone estimations are being extended into the upper air.

Traces of ozone in the air at ground-level are probably brought on wind currents from the ozone concentrations in the stratosphere. Measurements of changes in the ozone of our low-level air can give us a clue to conditions in the upper air. They have become an aid to weather study and forecasting.

As ozone determination has extended to many parts of the world a picture is being built up of the general distribution of ozone in the air. Near the equator the air contains only small amounts of ozone. The amount increases as we move to higher latitudes, and its seasonal and daily variation increases. In temperate regions ozone reaches its maximum concentration in the spring, and throughout the year there are considerable changes in ozone from day to day.

These daily variations are connected with the depressions and anticyclones which dominate our weather. Areas of high ozone in the air are associated with low-pressure areas.

Although ozone is being brought down incessantly from the stratosphere by atmospheric turbulence, its life in the air near the ground is short. Ozone is an active gas and will attack particles of soot and smoke or other organic materials in the air. Over cities and towns the ozone content of the atmosphere is particularly low. In the country and at the seaside there is usually a little more. But the seaside does not have more ozone in its air than does the country. The characteristic tang of seaside air is more likely to be due to decomposing fish.

The smell of ozone is a characteristic one; it is the smell associated with electric sparks. The name ozone was given to the gas a century ago, derived from the Greek *ozo*, I smell. Pure ozone is almost black.

Although ozone is nothing more than oxygen with its atoms arranged in threes, it is a violently active and explosive substance. It is made from oxygen by passing the gas through an electric discharge; as the ozone is formed it absorbs energy from the electric sparks. It is only too anxious to get rid of this extra energy and return to its more normal state of ordinary oxygen.

Unless pure ozone is handled with the very greatest care it will change back into oxygen and liberate its energy instantaneously. The oxygen is heated and expanded violently as it is formed, and the result is an explosion. Drops of liquid ozone can shatter a metal plate on which they fall.

It is this instability of ozone which is making it a useful industrial chemical to-day. As it decomposes ozone liberates its oxygen in an extremely active form. The oxygen will attack and combine with organic sub-

THE ANVIL OF A THUNDERCLOUD

LIGHTNING AND THUNDER

Nature's 100,000,000-volt spark heats the air to 15,000°C. in a fraction of a second. Explosive expansion of the air causes sound-waves that reach us as thunder.

stances, just as it does when ozone meets a particle of soot in the air. Moreover the only residue from ozone's decomposition is harmless oxygen. It forms no undesirable by-products.

For many years ozone has been used for purifying air. In 1911 an ozone plant was installed by the Central London Underground Railway to sterilize and purify the air circulating through the tunnels. Ozone gas was made by passing air through a space across which a silent electric discharge was flowing. The ozone formed was led into the ventilation air stream; as it met impurities and bacteria in the air the ozone liberated active oxygen that attacked the impurities and destroyed many of the harmful bacteria.

This system of air purification with ozone has now become widely used, and ozone has proved to be an effective germ destroyer even at concentrations of only one part in several million parts of air. Since 1946 improvements in equipment for 'ozonizing' air have brought down the cost of making ozone. It is competing effectively with other processes that are used industrially for providing active oxygen.

Sterilization of water, for example, is largely carried out with the help of chlorine. Chlorine kills the germs in the water by liberating active oxygen from the water, which attacks the germs. Ozone can do this job effectively, and the only residue it leaves in the water is a supply of sparkling oxygen. A plant producing 1250 pounds of ozone a day is used in Philadelphia for purifying the city's drinking water. Coke producers have installed ozone plants to destroy the noxious chemicals in waste liquors.

Bleaching is another process that relies on active oxygen. Chlorine, bleaching powder, and peroxides all depend on the liberation of oxygen to remove the colour from soiled materials. The oxygen converts the coloured substances to colourless ones. Ozone has been used successfully for bleaching wood pulps and for cotton.

In industrial processes, wherever active oxygen is needed, ozone has become a potentially valuable raw material. It is helping to make hormones and formalin, sulphuric acid, and dyes.

For most of these applications ozone is made on the spot by passing air through a silent electric discharge. Ozone itself is intractable and dangerous to store and carry about; its success has therefore depended on the design of cheap, efficient 'ozonizers' that could be installed where the gas was required. But ozone has now shown signs of becoming a raw material that can be handled in a conventional way. Methods have been found of handling liquid ozone safely.

During World War II German scientists were working on a plan to bombard New York with rockets launched in Europe, 4000 miles away. Ozone was to be the propellant, but it was found too dangerous. It tended to detonate spontaneously with tremendous violence.

Since the war American scientists have developed methods of storing liquid ozone. Its energy release can now be controlled, and it may well prove to be a fuel that will lift us through the atmosphere on our first flights into space.

In 1785 the Hon. Henry Cavendish carried out an experiment in which he tried to eliminate each of the known constitutents of the air. He removed the oxygen and nitrogen, the carbon dioxide and the water. But no matter what he did Cavendish could not destroy a last little bubble of gas. This gas, representing about 1/200 of the air, seemed to be something that differed from any of the known atmospheric gases.

More than a century later another great British

chemist, Lord Rayleigh, noticed that nitrogen made by removing the other gases from air was always a little heavier than nitrogen generated from its chemical compounds. Atmospheric nitrogen was apparently contaminated with a small amount of some other gas from the air. In May 1894 Professor William Ramsay isolated this new constitutent of the air. It was given the name argon.

The most astonishing characteristic of argon was its chemical inertness. Nitrogen itself is a gas that will not easily combine with other elements; but compared with argon it is a chemical firebrand. Argon showed no inclination at all to join forces with other atoms. It was this chemical indifference that had enabled argon to escape detection for so long, even though it forms one per cent. of the air. It took no part in any of the chemical unions that can imprison oxygen and nitrogen.

The discovery of argon in the air little more than half a century ago was surprising enough. But there was more to come. Careful examination of the atmospheric argon showed that it was, in fact, a mixture of several gases. Liquid ' argon ' was distilled and separated painstakingly into its constituents. In addition to argon it contained four other gases : helium, neon, krypton, and xenon.

Like argon these gases are entirely inert and unresponsive. They form a new class of elements which are characterized by their chemical idleness. The existence of argon, neon, krypton, and xenon was virtually unsuspected until they were discovered in the air; helium had been identified some little time before. During the eclipse of the sun observed in India in 1868 scientists had found that the wave-lengths of light emitted by the sun could not be accounted for entirely by known elements. The sun must contain an element that had not then been discovered on earth; it was given the name helium. In 1882 a study of the wave-lengths of light emitted by the flames from Vesuvius showed that this same helium was among the gases being blown into the atmosphere.

During his research that followed the discovery of argon in the air Professor Ramsay found that helium was imprisoned in cleveite and other minerals; the gas driven from these minerals when they were dissolved in acid emitted the yellow light of helium. Since then helium has been found in the gases from many natural springs, and it is present in underground deposits of natural gas in the United States.

The discovery of this strange new class of elements was of the very greatest academic interest. But their chemical inertness appeared to condemn the gases to a life of modest industrial value. During the last twenty years the liquefaction of air and the separation of its components have made the inert gases available in commercial quantities. And each has found a market in helping to satisfy one or other of the complex needs of the modern world.

Helium, first of the rare gases to be discovered, is present to the extent of only five parts per million in the air. But some of the natural gases associated with petroleum deposits contain as much as 8 per cent. of helium. It is from this source that most of the world's supply of helium is drawn. The increasing use of natural gas as fuel in the United States has meant that vast amounts of helium are being lost into the air; the helium passes through the gas flame unchanged. Pure helium is extracted from selected wells; a plant in Texas is operated by the Bureau of Mines who supply helium of more than 99 per cent. purity.

Few countries outside North America have reserves of natural gas, and the United States holds a virtual monopoly of helium from this source. The United States

Government controls the export of the gas, and helium is comparatively rare and expensive in other countries.

In Northern Italy helium is present in the gases thrown out by the volcanic steam jets of Tuscany. These jets have been tapped as sources of power at Lardarello; helium may become a by-product of real importance.

The source of the earth's helium is something of a mystery. In the mineral cleveite the gas is a product of radio-active decay of other elements in the mineral. Helium is absorbed inside the mineral and is released when the cleveite is dissolved in sulphuric acid. Helium in the huge underground reservoirs of natural gas, on the other hand, cannot be a result of local radio-active decay; there are no large deposits of radio-active minerals in the vicinity of the gas. It is possible that the helium has seeped through from rocks lying deeper in the earth.

Helium isolated from the air contains about one part per million of helium (3). This is a form of helium in which the atoms are lighter than in normal helium. But helium from natural gas has only about one-tenth of this amount of helium (3), suggesting that its origin is not the same as that of atmospheric helium.

Although helium is such a minor constituent of the earth's atmosphere, it plays a more exciting role in the activities of the incandescent elements that form the sun. The sun is an atomic-energy factory operating on a fantastic scale. The process used is similar to that which releases energy in the hydrogen bomb; hydrogen is turned to helium, and the excess energy liberated is the fuel that maintains the tremendous heat of the solar furnace. The concentration of helium on the sun is steadily increasing.

Helium's reluctance to join forces with other elements in chemical unions is reflected in its behaviour when it is cooled. Atoms of helium have no great enthusiasm one for another, and helium is one of the most difficult of all gases to liquefy. The atoms prefer to retain their independence and stay in the form of gas. In spite of this helium can be liquefied at a low enough temperature. But no matter how much further it is cooled it will not solidify unless it is under tremendous pressure. Liquid helium does not possess a normal freezing point. When liquid helium is cooled it changes from one form of liquid into another. This super-cooled liquid helium, called helium II, behaves unlike an ordinary liquid. It defies the law of gravity, flowing upwards over solid surfaces. Helium II will climb the wall of its container and flow over the rim at the top. A ship would gradually sink if it was floated in helium II; the liquid would flow up the outside of the ship and down into the hold, seeking to balance the liquid levels inside and outside just as though the ship was holed.

Helium II finds its way through the tiniest cracks and pores which would be impervious to most liquids. It flows through narrow tubes and orifices without being held back by friction against the walls; it has no viscosity. As it emerges from a fine slit helium II is warmer than it was originally.

Helium II will conduct heat a million times more efficiently than does an ordinary liquid. The heat travels through the liquid helium in waves, like sound waves through the air. In very cold helium II heat travels at more than 100 feet per second.

This peculiar form of liquid has kept the world of science guessing; it is like a fourth state of matter that lies outside the normal gas, liquid, or solid.

Helium gas has established many commercial outlets. It is the lightest of all gases after hydrogen and is also non-inflammable. In the United States, where helium is available in quantity, it is the ideal gas for lifting airships and balloons.

Mixed with oxygen, helium makes a first-rate atmosphere for use in high-pressure work. Helium is only half as soluble as nitrogen in human blood; it is less liable to appear in the blood as the small bubbles of gas which cause ' the bends ' when pressure is released.

Wherever an inert, protective atmosphere is needed helium is being used. It prevents corrosion of metal surfaces during welding; it fills the glass containers in which the parchments of the United States Declaration of Independence and the Constitution are preserved.

Argon, available in almost unlimited quantities from the air, has had a less interesting but possibly more useful career than helium. Its main commercial outlet has been in electric light bulbs. Argon is so inactive that it does not affect the white-hot tungsten filament in the bulb.

Neon, also, has made its career in the electrical industry. But it is not the inertness alone of neon that has made it valuable; it is the bright red glow that the gas emits when it carries electric current. Neon has given its name to the discharge lamps that are used so lavishly in the world of advertising.

Krypton was of little commercial consequence until it was found better than argon for filling electric bulbs. Krypton-filled bulbs give a fifth as much light again as do argon-filled bulbs. But the relatively high cost of krypton restricted its use to special-purpose lamps, such as those that are used in mining.

During the war lamps were needed which could provide an instantaneous flash of high-intensity light for photographic reconnaissance work. It was found that krypton-filled tubes will resist the passage of electricity until a heavy voltage forces the gas to conduct the current. Suddenly, with an intense flash of light, a spark jumps through the tube under the terrific electrical pressure. The flash lasts a few millionths of a second, but it can deliver a beam of three billion candlepower, more brilliant than any conventional searchlight.

Krypton flashes of this sort have been used in peacetime for lighting airfields covered by fog. The instantaneous flash lights up the landing strip, but it is over too quickly to blind the pilot with its glare.

Xenon, rarest of all the inert atmospheric gases, is even more effective than krypton in these flash-discharge tubes. Xenon gives half as much light again as the spark jumps through the gas. These flashes can be made to follow each other rapidly, 4000 times a second and more. They will take a succession of photographs of objects moving at incredible speed. Xenon flash photography, for example, is used by physicists to follow the paths of sub-atomic particles as they fly through space.

11

The Floating Population

A SHAFT of sunshine piercing a darkened room will sparkle and glitter with a myriad tiny lights. Each light is reflected by a floating particle too small to make its own impression on the naked eye. The air we breathe is teeming with these specks of matter; a thousand million and more will dance in the air of a normal kitchen. Amongst them are particles of dust and dirt; there are tiny grains of pollen and fibres rubbed from our clothes; there are microbes, some harmless and others that cause disease; there are spores and fungi searching for a congenial place in which to settle down and grow.

These airborne particles are swept aloft to the stratosphere and blown over oceans and continents by ever-moving winds. Sometimes they settle on the surface of the earth, but the air is forever sustaining its supplies. As the wind sweeps over the fields it will lift the fine, dry particles of soil, carrying them aloft in clouds that darken the sky. From the Dust Bowl region of the United States, where feckless cultivation has stripped the land of its natural strength, the wind has whisked away millions of tons of topsoil that may have taken a thousand years to form. Swept aloft, the fine particles have settled as dust over towns and cities thousands of miles away.

Wherever volcanoes are exploding their charge of rocks and magma, fine particles of ash are being blown with shattering violence into the air. Vast clouds of volcanic ash will float for years in the upper atmosphere. When Krakatoa erupted off Java on August 27, 1883, an entire island was disintegrated and blown as dust into the air. For years clouds of fine ash were wafted round the world at a height of between five and fifteen miles.

Every day millions of meteors dive from space into the atmosphere of the earth. As they roar through the air they are heated by friction until they explode into clouds of fine fragments. Most of the meteors disintegrate as the air begins to thicken at a height of about fifty miles. Sometimes a meteor will reach the earth to blast an immense crater a mile or more across. Day after day these meteors bring enough dust to the atmosphere to double the earth's weight by the year 3000 million million A.D.

As the wind blows over the sea the salt spray is swept into the air. The water evaporates, leaving ultra-fine particles of salt to mingle with the dust.

During summer, flowers in their ecstasy will throw out pollen in clouds that fill the air with billions of golden grains. Swept towards the stratosphere, pollen is carried immense distances by the wind. It falls over ships hundreds of miles out to sea; it settles in great drifts on the forest floor.

Mingling with all these particles of solid matter are tiny living things. Germs and micro-organisms ride aloft on the dust and droplets in the air. Many are harmless to human beings; yeasts and moulds ask for nothing more exciting than a crust of bread on which to grow or a vat of sugary liquid to ferment. Bacteria may be seeking for dead organic matter, like leaves that have fallen from the trees, or the carcase of an animal. Some of the bacteria are disease producers that will multiply if they can enter our bodies from the air; these are the germs breathed out by people suffering from disease.

Coughs and sneezes can fill the air with countless tiny droplets. Some will fall to the ground, but many will float about, perhaps to be inhaled by other people. Inside these droplets are viruses and germs that can be the cause of tragic epidemics.

In industrial countries, where people are crowded together in factories and offices, in buses and trams, the air-borne germs are given every opportunity of spreading their diseases far and wide. The air, with its floating microbe population, has become the route over which many epidemics travel. Air-borne respiratory infections, for example, cause more than a third of all industrial absences.

These living and inanimate floating particles, together with the dirt and smoke we disgorge from our furnaces and fires, can fill the air to the extent of 100 million in every cubic foot. The air of a small room could supply each person on earth with many specks of dust or dirt.

The unseen particles in our atmosphere affect our lives in many ways. The beauty of the skies is a gift that comes to us from the particles floating in the air. As sunlight penetrates our atmosphere its rays are scattered and reflected by the particles it meets. But the bands of light of different wave-lengths that combine to form the colourless light of day are affected differently by the particles. The short-wave rays that colour the blue end of the rainbow spectrum are scattered more efficiently than are the longer red rays. As we look up to the sky we are seeing the blue rays that have been scattered and reflected earthward from the sun's rays by the particles in the atmosphere. The blue of the sky is an illusion; we are really seeing blue rays from sunshine that would otherwise have missed us altogether.

When we look directly at the source of the sunlight the situation is reversed. The rays that are coming straight towards us are those remaining after the atmospheric particles have done their work. They are the red and orange rays that are not scattered during their journey through the air; the blue rays have been reflected and lost in transit. For the beauty of a deep red autumn sunset, therefore, we must thank the airborne particles that have filtered out the blue light from the sunshine. After Krakatoa had filled the air with its filmy curtain of dust in 1883 the world saw some of the most wonderful sunsets ever known.

Most of the dust and dirt floats in the lower levels of the air; it thins out rapidly above 3000 feet. The stratosphere is almost free of floating debris. As we rise higher into the air the blue of the sky gives way to purple and eventually to black; there is nothing in the air to break up the scorching rays of the sun.

Particles floating in the atmosphere can affect the climate and weather in several ways. Volcanic dust will draw a veil over the world that restricts the supplies of sunshine reaching the earth's surface. After Krakatoa's eruption the climate of the countries of the northern hemisphere became colder by a few degrees for two or three years. Astronomers at the Montpellier Observatory in France found that the dust cloud decreased the sunshine by a tenth. It is possible that the great ice-ages of the past were due in part to volcanic upheavals that enveloped the world in dust.

Without its millions of particles the air would find great difficulty in releasing its moisture in the form of clouds and fog. Droplets of liquid water tend to grow around the particles, particularly those that will attract water, such as salt or chemical tars. Water released from clean air near the ground would saturate every solid surface in a super-dew.

The floating particles, in addition to providing nuclei for the water droplets, will encourage the air to release its moisture by helping to cool it. When the sun goes down the particles absorb heat from the surrounding air and may cool it to the point where liquid water appears.

Many of the particles that foul the air of our towns and cities are generated by our fires and furnaces. They create a problem in themselves, described in the following chapter. Nature herself, with her meteors and volcanoes, her soil and microbes, has filled the air with countless particles since the earth was born. When man appeared on earth he had to learn to live with these particles as part of his natural environment. And he has adapted himself to the conditions that he found. The human body operates on the assumption that there are particles in the air and has developed methods of dealing with them.

Many of the finest particles are inhaled and exhaled without staying in the lungs. Large particles are trapped in the air passages before they can reach the lungs. The dangerous particles are those of intermediate size, which can enter the lungs and stay there.

It is a strange fact that, under natural conditions, the air contains few of these difficult medium-sized particles. They come mostly from human activities such as mining and quarrying, and from industry and the domestic fire.

Once they have been deposited in the lungs air-borne particles can either dissolve and enter the body or remain embedded in the tissue of the lung. If they are absorbed their effect on the body depends on their toxicity. They may be harmless and be removed from the bloodstream by the liver or the kidneys. Or they may be sufficiently poisonous to damage some part of the body and prove fatal.

Insoluble particles retained in the lung can cause permanent tissue changes. They may encourage respiratory disease such as tuberculosis. Silicosis is a disease caused by the particles of silica dust that float in the air of mines. These particles are of a size that the body has not learned to cope with.

The damage caused by dangerous particles such as these, by industrial fogs and fumes, and by disease-producing microbes in the air, has stimulated research on the problem of removing fine particles from the air. Hospitals and pharmaceutical factories, for example, need air that is free from dangerous germs. Many industrial processes can operate only in air that is free from dust and dirt; photographic film cannot be made in air from which particles may settle.

Most of the methods of removing particles from the air depend on being able to make the particles touch a surface. This can be the surface of another particle or of a drop of water or the wall of the vessel through which the air is moving. The ease with which this contact can be made depends on the size of the particles. In still air particles larger than 1/2500 of an inch, such as fine face powder, will gradually settle out on their own. Particles less than 1/250,000 of an inch, such as those of tobacco smoke, will float in the air without showing any inclination to settle.

Both ranges of particles, the large and the small, can be removed fairly easily from the air. The large ones have sufficient inertia to be able to bump against a solid surface in their path; the small ones are knocked on to surfaces by the molecules of the air itself. But the particles in between are too small to bump against a surface on their own account and too large to be knocked about by the atmospheric molecules. These are the particles that are particularly difficult to remove from the air.

In most air-conditioning systems solid particles are trapped by passing the air through a filter. As it flows through the tight-packed fibres of paper or cloth the air has to twist and turn over a tortuous path. Its particles are flung one way and then the other until they bump against the surface of a fibre, and stick. Simple filters based on paper can remove all but a thousand of the 20,000 particles in a cubic inch of air. Some special filters, made from extra-fine asbestos fibres, will allow, on average, only one of the 20,000 particles to escape. They will remove bacteria, and the air that emerges is virtually sterile.

High-speed water sprays are used, the fast-moving water droplets bumping up against the floating particles and sweeping them away to the drain. In industrial dust-removers air or other gases are whirled through spiral ' cyclones ' in which the particles are flung against the walls by centrifugal force. In ultrasonic precipitators high frequency vibrations are fired into the air, making the particles vibrate to and fro, bumping against each other until they build up into particles large enough to settle. Floating particles are also caught by electrical precipitation. Air passes over an electrically-charged plate, which gives the floating particles an electric charge. As they flow along the particles pass another plate carrying an opposite electric charge. The particles are attracted to the plate, where they collect and can be removed.

Devices of this sort are effective so long as they are part of a system that can keep the air under control. Air flowing into a building through an air-conditioning plant can be cleaned in the knowledge that the clean air will not be contaminated by dirty air brought in through windows and doors. Modern buildings are designed in such a way that ventilation can be controlled effectively. But in the ordinary house ventilation is usually so haphazard that dust removal is impracticable. Clean air brought into the house through a filtration device would be contaminated by air swept in through windows, doors, and ventilators.

Electrostatic precipitators have been produced for domestic use and are effective when the ventilation of the house has been adequately planned. These precipitators can remove 90 per cent. of the air-borne dust and floating particles.

In most of these methods of cleaning the air removal of dust and other inanimate, floating particles implies removal of the germs as well. Germs are associated with the dust and moisture droplets. Where it is impossible to sterilize the air sufficiently by one or other of these methods direct attacks are made on the germs. Ultraviolet lamps will destroy germs in the air; it is the ultraviolet rays which give sunshine much of its bactericidal effect. In schools and hospitals ultra-violet lamps can cut the spread of infection by a half. Ozone, glycol, and other disinfectants can do much to sterilize the air of public buildings, where people are constantly bringing in reinforcements of germs from elsewhere.

During the last few years a new type of dust has been flowing into the air, bringing with it a threat more serious than that from any other source. Huge clouds of dust have been blown to heights of 25 miles and more from hydrogen and other atomic explosions fired off in Russia, Australia, the United States, and the Pacific islands. This dust is dangerous; it is radio-active, and its subatomic rays can be lethal.

As it explodes the atom bomb makes a huge fireball in the air. Inside the inferno the atomic fuel is disrupted into different elements. The bomb casing, the minerals of the earth, and anything else in the vicinity are affected by the atomic radiations that are generated by the million-degree explosion. These by-products from the bomb are radio-active; they fire off atomic rays as they change spontaneously into other elements.

Some of the radio-active by-products are short-lived; others will go on shooting out their rays at danger strength for years. Strontium 90, one of the products of uranium fission, takes 25 years for its radio-activity to diminish by half.

In the instant after the explosion a cloud of steam forms in the region of the fireball. The blast tears down to earth, stirring up a dust storm that is then sucked up towards the centre of the explosion by the fierce upsurge of heated gases.

The result is the familiar mushroom cloud, built up by the dust and vapour from the earth joining up with the nucleus of the original explosion. Inside this cloud billions of dust and water droplets are carrying radiation caused by the atomic split.

A lot of the radio-active dust settles gradually to earth round the area of the explosion. Over it scientists move cautiously with their ray detectors, waiting for the radiation to die down to a safe level. But a vast cloud of water and dust is swept into the upper air, where it is caught up and wafted away by winds that may blow at two hundred miles an hour or more.

Soon this radio-active cloud is scattered and dispersed and the intensity of radiation is diluted until it is no longer regarded as dangerous. But what goes up must come down. The radio-active dust from explosions in America, Russia, Australia, and the Pacific islands is now settling slowly over the earth and will go on doing so perhaps for years to come.

Atomic scientists assure us that the concentration of radio-activity in this dust is too low to do us any harm. And from the short-term point of view they are on safe enough ground. But the problem of radio-active damage is a complex one, and there are dangers inherent in this airborne dust that are making many scientists stop and think.

Already many atomic explosions have taken place. More and bigger ones are planned. Experimental bombs may be fired off in which materials such as cobalt are included to boost up production of high-strength radio-active by-products. Up into the air is going a stream of radio-active dust, which looks like increasing from year to year. Who knows for certain that this dust is not storing up disaster for us in years to come? Who can say that the small concentrations we are sending up now will not accumulate until they have reached danger point?

The assurances we are given about the danger from radio-activity are concerned mostly with its direct effects on the body. The rays fired off from radio-active substances can damage and destroy living cells. But a certain concentration of rays is needed before real damage can be done. This is the threshold concentration below which the radio-activity is considered harm-less.

It is this direct damage from radio-activity that we are particularly concerned with after an atomic explosion has taken place. A high concentration of radio-active dust could cause immediate damage if it were to be blown on to a city. That is why such precautions are taken to ensure that the winds are blowing in the right direction when atom explosions are fired off.

Scientists have found ways of increasing our bodily resistance to radiation. Certain drugs give some protection against it. Mice have been protected by giving them doses of alcohol. And meat proteins seem to be able to increase our resistance in some little-understood way.

But radio-activity has another, more insidious effect on the human life. It can damage the genes, the repro-ductive cells of the body. And in so doing it can bring about changes in hereditary characteristics, which we call mutations.

Locked away inside our genes are the units which

determine the characteristics we pass on to our offspring. Damage to the genes can affect the nature of the child that is produced. Radiation can therefore influence the character of our descendants for generations to come. Or it can prevent us having any children at all.

Normally mutations take place spontaneously from time to time. Sometimes the change is for the better; often it is for the worse. Scientists have suggested that one cause of natural mutation may be the radiation that is always showering on to us from space in the form of cosmic rays.

By increasing the amount of radio-activity that is floating about we are increasing the chances of our genes being hit and damaged by a ray. And this time there is no question of any 'threshold' concentration of radio-activity below which no damage is done. The more rays there are, the more chances there are that a gene will be destroyed or damaged. Once this happens there is no way of repairing the damage that has been done.

In these drifting clouds of atomic debris we have a danger to the human race. If ever atomic war should come and bombs were dropped in great quantities it could well mean the end of life on earth. Not necessarily through the direct effects of the atomic explosions but through the sterilizing effects of the radiations that lingered on in the atomic clouds.

As things are at present there is no immediate cause for alarm. But the over-enthusiastic firing-off of atom bombs even under peace conditions could well build up a radio-active smog that would mean real trouble for generations to come.

12

The Menace of Poisoned Air

DURING the early nineteenth century Londoners were
drinking raw river water pumped from the Thames and
distributed with all its filth and impurities to their
homes. One large water company had its intake pipe
within a few yards of the outlet of the great Ranelagh
Sewer. And epidemics of diseases like typhoid fever
were, naturally enough, the rule rather than the exception. To-day we spend millions of pounds a year to
ensure that our water is pure and wholesome by the
time it reaches the tap. And yet we seem to care little
about the purity of that other equally important neces-
sity of life—the air we breathe.

Every day we take into our lungs some thirty pounds
of air—four times the amount of food and water put
together. We need this air as a source of oxygen, which
'burns' our food and provides the energy to maintain
life. To release its oxygen to the body the air comes
into contact with a maze of tiny, delicate blood vessels
inside the lungs. These blood vessels are all too easily
damaged; and yet they must be working at full efficiency
if the body itself is to remain in health. Damage our
lungs, and we damage our ability to live a normal
vigorous life.

In many parts of Britain, and indeed in every industrial country in the world, the air we breathe is as dirty
and dangerous as water taken directly from a sewage-
polluted river. Into the air of our industrial areas we

spew a never-ending stream of smoke and grime, gases, and chemicals such as we would hesitate to inflict upon our enemies in times of war. Yet this is the air we are content to take into our lungs and into our children's lungs at the rate of more than a quarter of a hundred-weight a day!

Though industry is often called upon to take the blame for pouring its effluents into the air, the real culprit is to be found much nearer home. More than half the pollution of our atmosphere is caused by the ordinary domestic fire. A poisoned atmosphere is the price we pay for the privilege of huddling around the comforting glow from the open grate.

Burned as we burn it in millions of fireplaces in Britain, coal provides us with a return of about a tenth of the heat available in it. The rest goes up the chimney, largely in the form of unburned particles of carbon or as unburned gases and volatile substances driven off from the coal as it is heated.

In the smoke that pours from our house and factory chimneys the particles of carbon are so small that they float about in the air like a gas, and there is virtually no limit to their powers of penetration. Small solid particles in smoke, which may measure only a twenty-millionth of an inch in diameter, have no difficulty in finding their way into our lungs. They will float around in the air, often associated with sticky tarry substances, forming a smoke pall that hangs almost permanently over some industrial districts. In the air of the smoky cloud there are also supplies of chemicals produced from the burning coal. Sulphur dioxide from the sulphur in the coal, for example, will turn into sulphuric acid in the air.

The scale of air pollution caused in this way is so immense that it staggers the imagination. In Britain nearly two and a half million *tons* of smoke are released into the air every year, 1,290,000 tons of this coming from domestic fires, 700,000 tons from industry, 400,000 tons from the railways, and 10,000 tons from electricity generating stations.

Added to these figures for smoke there are over half a million tons of ash and five million tons of sulphur dioxide—equivalent to eight million tons of sulphuric acid. And this in a country whose industry was threatened in 1951 by a general shut-down due to shortage of sulphuric acid. The eight million tons we release into the air is about four times the total annual output of our sulphuric-acid industry.

Where air pollution is at its worst—in London and the overcrowded industrial regions of the North—the deposits of dirt are easy enough to see as they settle in a sticky, corrosive layer. Five hundred tons to the square mile every year is the deposit in many places—about four hundredweights of filth descending on an average small garden. But billions of floating particles in the air are even better able to impress their presence on us in the form of fog.

When moisture-laden air is cooled it releases some of its moisture as tiny droplets which collect around solid particles in the air. Smoke particles form ideal nuclei, and the corrosive, acrid fogs we know in London and over industrial areas are the result.

These smoke fogs, or smogs, are very different from the mists that float over smoke-free areas. In place of the water droplets surrounding the particles of dust in the air, we have droplets formed from solutions of sulphuric acid and other chemicals which have collected round tarry particles of carbon in the smoky air. These are the foul impurities we take into our lungs with our 30 pounds of air a day.

So much for the facts of what we are up against in air pollution. What actually are the effects of these air

impurities on our daily lives? Is the danger a real one
or is it exaggerated?

The obvious place to start in any assessment of the
menace of air pollution is to examine its effect on health.
And there is plenty of expert scientific and medical
opinion available.

According to a report of the Mellon Institute of
Medical Research, "more people are devitalized, dis-
abled, and poisoned by the impurities contained in
smoke-polluted air than by the noxious ingredients in
food and water."

During the week ended December 13, 1952, when
London was in the grip of the great fog, 4703 persons
died in the Greater London area. The figure for the
corresponding week of 1951 was 1852. A large part of
the increase was undoubtedly due to the blanket of choking smog that settled over the capital during that week.

Statistical evidence has shown that deaths from pul-
monary and cardiac diseases increase in proportion to
the increase in intensity and duration of smoke fog. The
mortality rate for children under five increases to a
maximum in industrial zones. The increase is attributed
by medical experts to the smoke pall covering these
districts.

Wherever there is smog, bronchitis and pneumonia
are prevalent. Elderly people with a tendency to bron-
chial catarrh are the first to succumb. By irritating the
lungs and air passages smog increases the breathing
difficulties of anyone who is suffering any form of chest
complaint. For example, tuberculosis.

This direct effect of airborne dirt is the most obvious
of its threats to health. But there is another factor which
is vitally important, particularly in a country like
Britain, that receives only a restricted ration of sunshine. And that is the effect of smoke and fog upon our
supplies of daylight.

Sunlight is essential to our bodily and mental health. The ultra-violet radiation in sunlight helps the body to make its supplies of vitamin D, which is needed for the healthy growth of body tissues. Lack of vitamin D— through lack of sunshine, for example—can lead to rickets.

Sunlight also plays a vital psychological role in life. Darkness and gloom are depressing to us all. Sunlight has a stimulating effect; it helps to maintain our vigour and vitality.

Floating about in the air above us, the pall of smoke from our chimneys cuts off an impressive proportion of sunshine that ought to be reaching people in our industrial areas.

In Manchester, suburbs in the north-eastern areas receive only a half or less of the sunshine that reaches suburbs in the south-west. The rest of the precious light is cut off by the pall of smoke that is blown eastwards across the area by prevailing winds.

In a study of cancer rates in 1947 Dr P. Stocks, Chief Statistician to the General Register Office, found that the mean annual hours of sunshine " significantly correlated with death rates from lung cancer, bronchitis, and tuberculosis, for which the strength of the correlation appears to be much greater for lung cancer than for other lung affections." Smoke in the air thus appears to be an important factor in producing cancer of the lung. This is not surprising. It is well enough known that cancer can be started on the skin of animals by means of certain chemicals, some of which are present in tarry materials such as those associated with smoke.

As a menace to health these airborne impurities are dangerous enough. But there are plenty of other crimes that our smoke must answer for. Not least is the economic loss that follows a period of fog and smog.

A million pounds would not cover the cost of fog to our airlines during winter months. The bill for traffic hold-up and dislocation on our roads and railways cannot easily be assessed, but undoubtedly it runs to several million pounds.

Any city dweller knows how smog can stunt and destroy the plant life struggling to exist in grimy parks and gardens. Research has shown that the growth of plants can be correlated with the amount of soot deposited from the air. Lettuce grown where the soot fall is only 42 tons to the square mile in a year is more than three times the weight of similar plants grown in industrial areas with a fall of 500 tons to the square mile.

In addition to cutting down the available sunshine energy the smoke forms a layer of dirt on the leaves of the plant, sealing it off still more from the sun and choking the pores through which the plant breathes. Moreover the acids in the air eat into the tissues of the plant; corrosive chemicals settle on the soil, destroying its fertility and killing off the useful micro-organisms.

In Manchester's parks alone some £1500 a year is the price paid in replacing plants which have been unable to live in the smoke-laden air. Under normal conditions the cost would be less than £100. In a country like Britain, where industrial areas are surrounded by nursery land that provides much of our fresh vegetables, polluted air must cost us tremendous food losses every year.

In our towns and cities we can see at a glance how the smoke-laden, corrosive air has eaten into buildings and property. Building deterioration in Britain due to atmospheric attack is estimated at £60 millions a year. Sulphur is the chief offender, with soot and tar acting as carriers which cling tenaciously to the stone, enabling the acids to do their work. The cost of repair to the Houses of Parliament stonework due to acid attack from the air has been put at a million pounds. Penetration of airborne acids into the stone is found at depths of twenty inches. The production of crystals inside the stones can peel off slabs of stone weighing two tons or more.

To the housewife who is trying to keep a decent, clean home the battle against smog is an everyday affair. The weekly wash in an average small home in Manchester takes an hour longer than it does in Harrogate. This represents a total time loss to Manchester families of five million hours a year. Add to this the extra cost in fuel and washing materials, estimated at 7½d. per week per household, and we have a further loss of £200,000 a year.

Taking everything into consideration the total cost of our smoke pall would be a fantastic figure. Direct losses in Britain have been estimated at roughly £100 million a year, with at least another £100 million to cover indirect losses. This annual bill presented to a hard-up nation takes no account of the greatest loss of all—the health and happiness that are drained away from the millions who must live in the shadow of our man-made clouds.

Nor do these losses caused by smoke include the initial wastage of coal inherent in smoke production. Soot and the chemicals pouring into the air as smoke are a valuable part of our coal. They represent loss of heat in that they have remained unburnt; and they include chemicals that are invaluable to us as industrial raw materials.

The soot that floats above us in our air is equivalent to three days' output of coal from all the mines in Britain. The chemicals that accompany it have been formed from the remains of plants that lived and died when the world was young. These chemicals are the starting materials for modern industries that make nylons and vitamins, dyes and drugs, plastics, insecticides, and paints.

When we burn raw coal we are burning these chemicals that could earn us so much if we turned them into the consumer goods we need. Instead, we are content to pour them out into the air to create the obnoxious filth that blights our lives and property.

We have been burning coal for hundreds of years as a source of heat. This heat is as essential to us to-day as is food. We need heat to warm our houses and cook our meals, to drive our trains and ships, and to provide the power that turns our factory wheels. Since the Industrial Revolution we have built our economy very largely on coal as a heat-producer. And in our smog we are now reaping where we have sown.

Six hundred years ago, when coal-burning was an offence punishable by law, there was some excuse for burning raw coal as a source of heat. To-day, when we know what chemical riches are to be found in coal and have learned how to process and burn our coal efficiently, there is no excuse for failing to put into practice what scientific experiment has made available to us.

When we squander our coal by sending nine-tenths of it up the chimney we are squandering our capital resources. Once the coal has gone from beneath our soil it has gone for good. And the days will come when we shall have to hoard our remaining stocks of coal, just as America was forced to hoard her fast-disappearing deposits of elemental sulphur.

If ever there was an urgent social problem for us to tackle in our welfare state it is this desperate menace of atmospheric pollution. Smog must go. But how?

Inevitably coal will remain our most important source of heat and power for many years to come. We have nothing that can take its place. Atomic energy, sun-

shine, tides, wind, and all the rest may help in time—
but only from a long-term point of view.

We must, therefore, make every effort to remove as
much as possible of the chemicals and volatile raw
materials from the coal before we burn it. And where
we are forced to use coal—for example, in industry,
where furnaces are designed for coal-burning—we must
ensure that the coal is burned efficiently and that harmful materials are removed as far as possible from the
effluents.

Removing the chemicals from coal is a job we do now
when we are making coke. Coal is heated in retorts,
and coal gas is driven off together with liquid chemicals
and coal tar. The coke is left behind in the retort.

In coke and coal gas we have two clean, smokeless
fuels. And in the chemicals from coal we have our raw
materials for a thousand new synthetic products from
nylon stockings to sulpha-drugs.

Coke and its related smokeless fuels made by ' pro-
cessing ' coal will burn cleanly and efficiently in modern
grates and stoves. They may not flicker attractively like
the coal we have grown accustomed to. But this is a
small price to pay in return for a supply of wholesome
air to breathe.

A simple ban on coal-burning would be economically
impossible in present circumstances. But smoke abolition
will have to come some time, and it might as well be
sooner than later. The important thing is to make a start.

In Britain this has now been done with the introduction of smokeless zones. To Coventry goes the honour
of establishing the first smokeless zone in the country.
The badly damaged central area of the city was declared
a smokeless zone on March 1, 1951. In this area of 30
acres it is an offence to pollute the atmosphere with
smoke; only smokeless heating appliances are permitted.

Manchester introduced a smokeless zone on May 1,

1952, covering 109 acres of the city. Other towns are following suit. In these smokeless zones all new property is being equipped with efficient grates and stoves that can burn smokeless fuels. New factories are installing plant to operate on a smoke-free basis.

This introduction of modern equipment is a relatively simple matter where new building is in progress, and there is an obvious attraction in creating smokeless zones in blitzed areas. Where industry is already established, modern scientific techniques can be used for cutting down air pollution.

By using gas-cleaning devices and by installing more efficient furnaces industry has done a great deal to help in cutting down air pollution. Very often the recovered material has become a valuable by-product which has helped to pay the cost of the installation. But the domestic fire must carry a major share of the blame for our smoke pall, and for this smokeless fuel is the only immediate answer.

Looked at from the point of view of the country as a whole, smokeless zones are insignificant in that they represent tiny islands in a vast ocean of smoke. In the zones themselves the inhabitants will probably notice little difference in the quality of their air. Smoke will pour into them from the surrounding districts. But the zones are an earnest of more to come. They represent that vital thing—action.

With a bit of luck, good sense, and good management we shall gradually extend the area of these zones until in due course the sun can get through to the whole of Britain again.

13

Turmoil in the Thundercloud

To primitive man the rumble of thunder was a measure of the anger of the Gods. Mighty Thor, powerful and beneficent, was taking up arms against the enemies of mankind; the heavens shook under the clash of the great warriors in the sky. To-day, as in those prehistoric times, the elemental fury of a thunderstorm can fill us with a sense of awe. The towering thundercloud, dark and menacing, carries within it mysteries that science has yet to solve.

The atmospheric conditions that can beget a thunderstorm have long been understood. When air near the ground is warm and moist it will tend to rise into the regions of thinner air above. Like a vast fountain of gas it shoots up into the higher levels of the troposphere. As it rises the air expands and cools to the point where it becomes overburdened with moisture. Water appears in the air, floating as billions of droplets that form the cottonwool cumulus cloud we see from the earth below. Near the top of the cloud, where temperatures are well below zero, the droplets freeze into particles of ice.

When conditions are favourable this column of moist, rising air will soar towards the base of the stratosphere itself. Within the towering cloud, six or seven miles high, thousands of tons of water have been carried aloft as vapour and released in the form of water and ice. This is the water that deluges the ground with rain as thunder and lightning fill the air with their fury. Soon the force of the rainstorm is spent; the lightning and thunder are gone, and a gentle drizzle marks the slow decay of the thundercloud.

This pattern of behaviour is characteristic of most thunderstorms, caused in one way or another by vigorous convection currents in the air. There is no mystery in the source of the rain, which comes from the moisture in the rising air. But of the manner in which the rain is formed and the way in which the electricity of the lightning flash is generated we know little.

Within the last decade a growing interest in the behaviour of the atmosphere has given a stimulus to thundercloud research. The inside of the cloud is being explored and its activities investigated with the help of modern instruments and techniques. Slowly we are learning something of the turmoil that takes place behind the sombre walls of the massive cumulo–nimbus that threatens us with its lightning and its rain.

In 1946 a large-scale investigation of thunderclouds was begun by American meteorologists. Co-operating in the research were the United States Air Force and Navy, the United States Weather Bureau, and the National Advisory Committee for Aeronautics. In charge of the project was Horace R. Byers, chairman of the University of Chicago department of meteorology.

Over an area of about a hundred square miles a network of meteorological stations was set up in Florida. As thunderstorms drifted overhead these stations recorded electrical and atmospheric conditions. Radiosonde balloons were sent up into the gathering storms, and planes flew through the clouds at various heights, carrying meteorological equipment with them.

During 1946 and 1947 more than 1300 thundercloud flights were made by a group of Northrup Black Widow night fighters at heights between one and five miles.

None of the planes suffered any mishap. Aboard the planes were instruments for measuring wind currents, moisture, air temperatures, and other atmospheric data. Radar was used to follow the courses of the planes and the balloons, and to detect the formation of ice and rain inside the cloud.

From the information gained during this research, meteorologists have been able to build up a picture of the movements and behaviour of the air inside a thundercloud and the conditions under which water droplets and ice particles are formed.

Inside the cloud several distinct storms are usually in operation at the same time. Each storm occupies a 'cell' in the thundercloud and is separated from the other storm centres by a wall of comparatively tranquil cloud. The base of the thundercloud as a whole may cover an area of 250 square miles or more, but each cell will be as little as three miles wide.

There are three clearly defined stages of development in a thunderstorm. As rising air sweeps aloft within the storm cells fingers of cloud may be lifted into the stratosphere itself. This uprush of air is the first stage in the development of the storm; it is the mechanism that provides the water supply. In little more than a quarter of an hour rising currents will have filled the air with billions of water droplets and particles of ice to a height of several miles.

During this build-up stage air is rushing into the base of the cloud at speeds of up to sixty miles an hour. The warm airstream is felt by people on the ground as a mild breeze. Often the inflowing air will 'cancel out' the movement of air caused by the prevailing wind that is blowing the storm centre along; this is the calm before the storm.

In the upper levels of the troposphere, where temperatures are well below zero, the discarded water is frozen

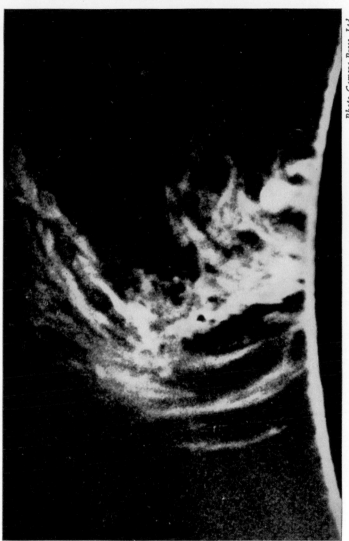

Photo Camera Press, Ltd.

SOLAR CORONA

This flare, thrown out from the surface of the sun, sends jets of high-speed particles into space. In the atmosphere of the earth they cause auroras.

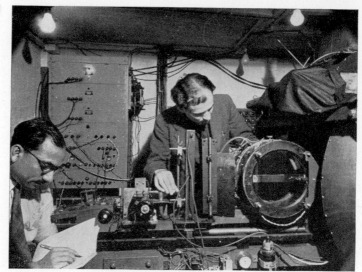

Photo "Picture Post"

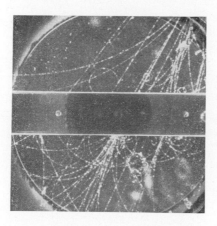

COSMIC-RAY
PHOTOGRAPHY

(*Left*) About twenty cosmic-ray particles enter the top of the cloud chamber. At least four of them penetrate the thick lead plate across the middle of the chamber. These penetrating particles can be distinguished easily by looking along the tracks from the edge of the photograph.

Photo Dr G. D. Rochester and Dr C. C. Butler, Physics Department, Manchester University into tiny particles of ice. These particles grow into larger ones, which begin to fall through the air under the pull of gravity. At first they fall more slowly than the speed of the rising air and make no progress towards the ground. But in time the burden of the water becomes too great for the rising air, and drops and particles pour down through the cloud. As they go they drag a stream of cold air with them. The thundercloud has now reached its second stage.

As the down-flowing air sweeps across the base of the cloud it smothers the rising current of warm, moist air and ultimately cuts it off entirely. The cold air streams on to the surface of the earth, deluging it with its accumulated stores of rain.

Inside the thundercloud this stage of maturity is marked by intense activity. The warm upstream and the cold downflow are racing past each other at 100 miles an hour or more. An aircraft flying through the storm cell meets severe turbulence. If the downflow is fast enough it will often carry hailstones from the upper layers of the cloud. Lightning darts from place to place within the cloud and from the base of the cloud to the earth; the air shakes with the rumble of thunder.

In half an hour the storm has died. The cell of the thundercloud is drained of its burden of water and the third stage has been reached. The storm cell begins to decay.

Meanwhile in other cells of the thundercloud storms may be at different stages in their development. Seen from below rain will often pour from one part of the cloud after another as individual cells reach maturity. Between the active cells are walls of cloud a mile or more wide.

The third stage of the storm is marked by a steady fall of gentle rain as the remaining moisture is dissipated. The top of the cloud assumes its familiar anvil shape as fine ice particles float away near the boundary of the stratosphere.

This pattern of thundercloud behaviour has emerged from the intensive work carried out during the great American thundercloud project and by meteorologists working on a less ambitious scale in many other countries. The recognition of well-defined storm cells within the cloud has suggested that, with adequate radar and other flying aids, aircraft will be able to fly through the calm areas of a thundercloud and avoid the turbulence of the active cells.

Most of the cloud floats above the freezing-point level in the air. The base of the cloud may be slightly above zero; but the top of the cloud is often at a temperature of below −40°F. At this temperature droplets of water will not exist as such in the cloud; they must freeze into ice particles.

In the central and lower portions of the cloud droplets of moisture will be super-cooled and probably coexist side by side with ice particles. The tendency will be, however, for the ice particles to grow in size at the expense of the water in the droplets.

As the ice particles grow into pellets of hail they will begin to fall through the air, collecting smaller particles as they collide with them during the descent. In the lower part of the cloud, liquid water droplets will predominate.

In spite of the deluge of water that pours from most thunderstorms only a small proportion of the water in the cloud actually reaches the ground as rain. Even so a storm can drench an area of a few square miles with 100,000 tons of water in a few minutes.

One-third of all the water taken up into the cloud remains as invisible water vapour in the air. Another third appears as rain but evaporates again during its descent through the cloud. Of the remaining water only

a third reaches the ground as rain—about a ninth of
the total water in the cloud. Some of the rest is lost
through the sides of the thunderstorm cell and some is
left behind in the decaying cloud.

During the mature stage of the cloud an electrical
situation is created which culminates in the lightning
flash. Lightning is simply an immense spark similar to
that which jumps between the terminals of an ordinary
electric battery. It marks an instanteous flow of electricity between points where the electrical pressure is high
enough to overcome the resistance of the air that
separates them. In an ordinary household electricity
system the electrical pressure that causes a spark to
jump is about 250 volts; in a typical thundercloud there
is often a pressure difference of some 100 million volts
between the top and bottom of the cloud.

As lightning darts through the cloud it helps to relieve
the great electrical pressure differences. But within a
few seconds the huge natural dynamo has recharged
itself, and flashes will follow each other at the rate of
about three a minute. Most of the lightning flashes we
see appear to be between the cloud and the ground.
But there are many more flashes inside the cloud itself;
we cannot see them so easily as the cloud-to-earth
flashes.

In Britain there are about five flashes inside the
average thundercloud for every flash that reaches the
earth. In South Africa, where thunderclouds ride higher
in the sky, less than one flash in ten is from the cloud
to the earth.

The scientific study of lightning has been going on
for more than two hundred years. During the early
eighteenth century, when the mysteries of electricity
were occupying the minds of scientists and philosophers,
a relationship was suspected between the lightning
flash and the electric spark. Benjamin Franklin, in

November 1749, suggested that an experiment should be made to try and identify lightning with electricity. In 1752 a French scientist called Dalibord showed that he could draw sparks from the bottom of a long iron rod reaching into the air during a thunderstorm. A few weeks later Franklin flew a kite beneath a thundercloud and found that electricity was flowing down the wet cord to the ground.

Though lightning has been recognized for so long as a mammoth electric flash, its cause and detailed behaviour have remained mysteries to the present time.

Immediately before and during World War II scientists at Kew carried out a series of experiments to extend our information about the electrical conditions in a cloud. Balloons equipped with recording instruments were sent up into thunderclouds. From these and other experiments it has been shown that there is an area of positive electric charge in the upper part of the thundercloud and a region of negative charge near the base of the cloud. Both regions are usually above the level at which the air temperature is below zero. In most clouds, also, a little region of positive electricity lies below the negative area at the base of the cloud.

Between the main areas of positive and negative charge there is an electrical pressure difference of as much as 100 million volts. This is the pressure that overcomes the resistance of the air in the cloud, allowing the huge lightning spark to pass. Similarly there is a huge difference in electrical pressure between the negative region near the base of the cloud and the earth below; if the cloud base is near enough to the ground the flash will pass to earth.

High-speed photographs of lightning flashes have shown that each flash involves several distinct strokes of electricity. The first stroke makes its way through the air in short steps, giving the flash its typical zigzag path.

Often it forks as it seeks out a route through the resisting air. Travelling at a speed of over 200,000 miles per hour, this leader stroke marks out a path for other strokes that follow in quick succession. The whole flash is over in a fraction of a second, one stroke following another with as little as 1/100 of a second between them. On the average three or four strokes make up the flash; sometimes there are as many as thirty or forty.

As it tears through the air the electricity in the lightning flash heats up a channel of air about six inches wide. Three-quarters of the energy of the flash is turned into heat that raises the temperature of the air to 27,000°F. in a matter of a few ten-millionths of a second. The air expands with explosive violence, creating the sound waves that reach our ears as thunder.

Although lightning is the most flamboyant method by which the thundercloud copes with its electrical pressure differences, it is not the only route through which electricity flows away. Wherever there are pointed objects on the earth, such as blades of grass or the leaves of trees, church steeples, and flagpoles, electricity flows from them into the highly-charged air above. Electricity will trickle away from a fence post into the air like water leaking through a hole in a bucket. During a thunderstorm the low-flying negatively charged base of the cloud encourages a flow of positive electricity towards it from the earth. This is the cause of the St Elmo's fire that dances on trees and poles when thunderclouds are about. In a similar way the positive electricity at the top of the thundercloud will leak away steadily towards the electrically charged air of the ionosphere.

Without these leaks to help clouds dissipate their electrical tension, lightning flashes would be more frequent than they are. A cloud can recharge itself with electricity in five to seven seconds after a flash has jumped. But it is some twenty seconds before another flash takes place; the delay is caused by the loss of electricity from the top and bottom of the cloud and by the ice particles and water droplets carrying away electricity as they fall through the cloud. Raindrops reaching the ground from a thunderstorm are usually carrying an electric charge.

Sometimes the lightning flash will leave a bead-like pattern of luminosity in the air. These isolated patches of glowing air, like the luminous fireballs which are seen when lightning is about, have not yet been explained satisfactorily. Some fireballs are only an inch or two across; others have been estimated as more than forty feet in diameter.

Many theories have been put forward to explain how the areas of positive and negative electricity are separated inside a thundercloud. Initially the air from which the cloud is made is electrically neutral, with positive and negative electric charges balancing each other out. Somehow during the mature stage of the storm huge areas of positive and negative electricity are forced apart, the positive electricity to the top and the negative to the base.

One of the most recent theories was described by B. J. Mason, of the Imperial College of Science and Technology, London, at the meeting of the British Association in 1953. When ice pellets are being formed from water droplets in the intensely cold upper regions of the cloud they become charged with negative electricity. A corresponding positive charge moves into the air, carried away perhaps by splinters of ice that break away from the pellet. As the pellets grow they begin to fall through the air, carrying their negative charge with them and leaving the positive charge behind in the upper air.

Experiments with artificial ice particles have shown that pellets made in this way are, in fact, negatively charged. And it has been calculated that this process could separate the electric charges in a thundercloud fast enough to account for lightning flashes.

The detection of thunderstorms has now become an established part of meteorology, and surveys of thunderstorm activity have been carried out. In Britain there are, on average, six lightning flashes to every square mile during the year. The world has an annual crop of more than 16 million thunderstorms, with 2000 or more in progress at any time. Every second the sky is lit by 100 lightning flashes.

Thunderstorm activity reaches its height in Britain during May and again in September, with the Manchester area, the Severn Valley, and Lincolnshire as the storm centres.

At all times the earth itself is negatively charged with respect to the electrically active air in the ionosphere to the extent of half a million volts. When the weather is calm positive electricity is steadily leaking down and collecting on particles in the air near sea-level. The air at roof-top level carries a charge of 1000 volts with respect to the ground.

During thundery weather the air is churned about and the particles of the lower air are borne aloft, taking their positive electricity with them. It has been suggested that this may in part account for the electrical charges in the thundercloud.

As lightning flashes to earth it carries great violence in its stroke. In some countries where thunderstorms are prevalent lightning kills three or four people per million of the population every year. Many lives are lost through sheltering under trees, which provide a short-cut route to lightning on its way to the ground. Small boats at sea and bathers on the shore can also attract the lightning towards them.

Lightning conductors will protect a building from

damage by offering an easy route to the electricity flowing towards the earth. By attracting the lightning to them they can keep it from striking unprotected buildings elsewhere.

14

The Mystery of the Merry Dancers

On an autumn night in 1585 thousands of terrified people fled from their homes in the peaceful French countryside, seeking the sanctuary of the Parisian churches. The sky, they believed, was on fire. Great curtains of light swept over the northern horizon. Huge beams probed up into a sky that was flickering with red and blue lights. Many believed that the end of the world had come.

But by morning the lights had faded and gone. The sky looked as peaceful and stable as usual. And the people crept thankfully from their churches back to the homes that had suffered no harm from the weird display of nocturnal light.

What the people had seen was the aurora borealis. The northern lights. In countries further north, in Scotland and Scandinavia, the aurora is a familiar sight and holds no terror. But as we move further south the lights become less frequent. In France and the Mediterranean countries they may be seen but once in a generation, striking awe into people who have often never heard of them before.

The lights can take on many shapes and forms. Often they appear simply as a glow that lights the northern sky. This may then spread out until it forms an enormous arc that spans the horizon. The arc will frequently stay unchanged throughout the night. Sometimes it becomes brighter, rising higher in the sky and then breaking into great folds of light like moving curtains drawn across the heavens.

Aristotle, writing about the aurora in his book *Meteorologica,* describes the black segment under the luminous arch as the ' abyss '; its blackness is intensified by contrast with the eerie light surrounding it. Pliny believed that the lights were a portent of evil events to come.

Often the lights will flicker, and the brightness will rise and fall. The arch becomes agitated as though tormented by some evil spirit. Suddenly huge rays will stab the surrounding darkness, shooting out into space as though searching for some intruder in the sky. These rays may glow with green or violet, pink or purple light. They are drawn together, converging towards a corona and forming a cone of light that makes the heavens seem on fire.

In the Shetland Isles, where the northern lights are often prancing across the sky, they are called the "Merry Dancers." Further south, in Britain and in France, we seldom see the full beauty and movement of the auroral displays, and they carry the more sedate description of the " Northern Dawn." This is the meaning of the name " aurora borealis," which a French philosopher gave to the lights in 1621.

Although the lights have been a familiar sight to northern peoples for thousands of years, they have remained a scientific mystery to this day. But within the last generation the lights have been the subject of research and we are now at least able to offer a reasonably satisfying explanation of them.

Observations have shown that the aurora is centred on the earth's magnetic pole in northern Greenland. The lights can be seen most frequently and with the greatest intensity on a line that roughly circles the magnetic pole, passing between Iceland and the Faero Islands, skirting the south of Greenland and the northern coasts of Europe and Asia. As we move north or south of this imaginary line the frequency of the aurora drops rapidly away.

In the Shetlands the northern lights can be seen almost one night out of three. In southern Scotland some twenty nights of the year have auroral displays. But in London there are only seven on the average every year.

This connection between the aurora and the magnetic north pole of the earth is duplicated in the Southern Hemisphere. Although observations are relatively few and far between, it is established that the southern counterpart to the aurora borealis, called the aurora australis, is centred on the magnetic south pole of the earth.

Although the aurora is so familiar a sight in northern lands, it is remarkably difficult to study in a scientific way. The lights are seldom still, flitting across the sky and appearing and disappearing without warning. We can draw them or photograph them easily enough. But the scientist searching for an explanation of a natural phenomenon likes to start by measuring it. With a few accurate facts and figures to play with he can get to grips with his problem.

One of the first auroral characteristics to be studied was its height. But with the aurora dancing about the sky in a state of unpredictable movement this presents some difficulties. A bright luminescent area may remain steady for a minute, or it may disappear in a few seconds.

In spite of the difficulties the height of auroral lights has now been estimated with the help of the traditional technique used in surveying mountains. The angle made by the summit is measured from two points as far apart as possible; if the distance between the points is known then the height of the summit can be worked out by simple trigonometry.

This technique was adapted to catch and measure the height of even the most transient of auroral lights by Professor Carl Störmer, of Oslo. Photographs of an auroral area are taken simultaneously by cameras several miles apart. Using the background of stars as reference points, the height of the aurora itself can be worked out.

Thousands of measurements have now been taken, and it has been found that the auroral lights are produced in the upper layers of the atmosphere. Sometimes the lights come from a height of only 60 miles. Claims are often made that auroral light has been seen below cloud level, but these are almost certainly due to light reflected by fog or mist.

Often the lights are as high as 600 miles and may at times originate from an area of full sunlight outside the earth's shadow. Usually, though, the auroral displays come from the atmosphere between heights of 60 and 200 miles.

Confirmation of these height measurements has come from another source in recent years. In 1947 scientists at Manchester University were using radar to study meteors. They found that echoes were also being sent back by areas of bright auroral light that happened to be in the sky. The height was estimated at about 250 miles.

Using this radar technique, Professor A. C. B. Lovell at Jodrell Bank Experimental Station in Cheshire has obtained echoes from auroral areas at heights of up to 600 miles. Similar results have come from radar experiments in Canada and Sweden. These measurements mean that the auroral lights are coming from the uppermost layer of the atmosphere, the ionosphere, where the atmospheric gases are extremely attenuated and easily influenced by electric charges.

So the area of auroral activity has become localized. It comes from the ionosphere in the regions above the north and south magnetic poles of the earth. But what of the light itself? What causes it? Is it, for example, sunlight that is being reflected or refracted by particles in the atmosphere so that it becomes visible on the dark side of the earth? Or is auroral light being generated in some way in the area of sky from which it appears to come?

If the auroral light was reflected sunlight it would have more than a superficial resemblance to the rainbow. The position of the rainbow in the sky is only an apparent one; it depends on the person who is seeing it. The light of the rainbow is reflected and refracted by raindrops in the air. But auroral light comes from a definite area of the sky. This area of the sky is itself aglow; its position is fixed and is not simply an apparent one. Moreover light that is reflected or refracted tends to become polarized—that is to say, the vibrations take place in restricted planes. Auroral light is not polarized and is therefore not reflected sunlight.

In this connection, the aurora must be distinguished from another form of nocturnal glow. Even when there is no moon the night is never so dark that we cannot see the outline of a tree or house against the sky. A little of this light comes from the stars, but most comes from the atmosphere itself. The upper layers of the air are glowing feebly all the time. We do not know how this glow is caused, but it appears to come from the sunlight that has been shining on to the earth during the day. Somehow the atmosphere is able to store up energy from the sun and emit it slowly again at night. It has been suggested that the sunshine separates the individual atoms of oxygen and nitrogen from one another; as they join together again they emit energy in the form of the light that shines on to us from the night sky.

Whatever may be the reason for this gentle night light provided by nature, it has no connection with the aurora. It is a steady background light that is overwhelmed by the majestic caperings of an auroral display.

To examine the nature of the light of the aurora itself scientists have used familiar techniques. Light is normally a mixture of waves of different lengths, and we can split any light into its constituent wave-lengths. These wave-lengths are determined by the nature of the material that is emitting the light. And by measuring and sorting out the wave-lengths in any light we can normally identify the substance or substances that are sending out the light, just as a criminal can be identified by the characteristic whorls and loops of his fingerprints.

Using spectroscopic methods of this sort scientists have shown that light from the aurora is being caused by atoms of oxygen and nitrogen from which electrons are being displaced. The light is, at least in part, emitted by these two normal constituents of the atmosphere which have somehow been excited by electrical agitation.

In 1939 it was discovered that hydrogen gas was present in the area of auroral light. This has since been confirmed by American scientists who have shown that the hydrogen atoms are in a state of rapid movement towards the earth. Calculations showed that they were approaching the earth at a speed of some 2000 to 3000 miles a second.

When auroral light is at its most intense this surge of fast-moving hydrogen particles is at its height. But there is normally only a trace of hydrogen in the atmosphere. Where, then, does the deluge of hydrogen atoms come from?

As this information on the nature of auroral light has accumulated, so has the relationship between the aurora and other natural phenomena become more clear. For a long time it has been known that the auroral lights come and go in cycles of increasing and decreasing intensity. In peak years the auroras are bright and frequent, their visibility reaching down into lower latitudes.

Observations going back over many years have shown that auroral intensity follows an eleven-year cycle. This is the same cycle that has been observed in sunspots, and the auroral cycle follows the sunspot cycle with the year of intensity lagging two years behind the year of maximum sunspot intensity.

This connection between the aurora and sunspot cycles gives us a direct clue to the origin and cause of the aurora. Detailed observations have taken the relationship a stage further, a large sunspot near the centre of the sun coinciding with intense auroral displays. The aurora, in fact, appears to be caused by the sunspot. But how?

The dark patches on the sun which we call sunspots are believed to be areas of intense activity. Great surges of atomic upheaval boil up from inside the sun. Accompanying these solar eruptions are huge flares that can be seen sweeping out from the sun's surface into space. And associated with the flares are streams of electrically charged atomic particles that are spewed out from the sun like water from a hose.

Can it be, then, that these huge jets of fast-moving atomic particles are responsible for the auroras in the upper layers of the earth's atmosphere? That is what scientists believe to-day. And the recent evidence of surges of hydrogen in auroral regions has pointed to the fact that the particles are electrically charged atoms of hydrogen gas.

Supporting this theory is further evidence of association with sunspot activity. Sunspots cause not only auroral activity but changes in the earth's magnetism as well. When sunspots are active the earth's magnetism is disturbed. Compass needles misbehave, and the earth acts as though it were a magnet influenced by tremendous electric currents passing near to it.

Immediately after a sunspot flare is seen there is a disturbance of radio communications over the sunlit area of the earth. And a day later comes the magnetic storm, the aurora, and a further disturbance of radio communications, less severe than the first but affecting the entire world. Electric currents set up in the earth's crust can be powerful enough to upset telephone communications as well.

These phenomena, including the aurora, which are associated with sunspot activity, are believed to be a result of light emission and the shooting out of electrically-charged particles from the sun. The almost instantaneous effect on radio is due to ultra-violet light which travels the distance between the sun and earth in a matter of minutes. The aurora and magnetic storm which follow later are caused by the stream of charged particles, which have taken almost a day to reach the earth.

As they reach the upper layers of the atmosphere the particles bombard the atoms of oxygen and nitrogen gas. The ionosphere becomes intensely activated and, instead of reflecting radio waves back to earth, it allows them to disappear out into space. At the same time the bombardment of the oxygen and nitrogen atoms dislodges electrons from their orbits in the atoms, which emit light as a result. This is the light we see as the aurora.

In a classic experiment carried out in 1897 the famous scientist Professor Birkeland showed how a stream of fast-moving atomic particles could produce an auroral effect in the laboratory. Birkeland used a little ball inside a glass apparatus. The ball was a magnet, like the earth, with a north magnetic pole and a south magnetic pole.

Birkeland fired a stream of electrons at the ball and found that they could be made to converge on two areas surrounding the poles. The magnetism of the ' earth ' was making the particles sweep round and reach the sphere in these auroral regions.

On the basis of this experiment Birkeland decided more than half a century ago that auroras were caused by streams of electrons fired off by the sun and sweeping in towards the earth. Caught up in the earth's magnetic influence, the electrons were attracted towards the north and south magnetic poles. And as they hit the particles of gas in the upper atmosphere they made the oxygen and nitrogen emit the auroral glow.

So the theory of particles from the sun is not a new one. But calculations showed that electrons alone could not be the cause. Until the discovery of the hydrogen stream the explanation of the aurora remained as much a mystery as it was before. The presence of fast-moving hydrogen in the upper atmosphere, however, is convincing evidence that hydrogen jets from the sun are probably the cause of the aurora. Sweeping in towards the earth's magnetic poles, these electrically charged hydrogen atoms excite the oxygen and nitrogen atoms and make them emit the auroral light. Streams of hydrogen are being constantly thrown out by the sun. They are not directed at the earth, but the earth is in the way of some of them. When this happens we get the auroras and the electric and magnetic storms. Although a lot of hydrogen reaches our atmosphere in this way, little of it penetrates to lower levels. Unlike the sun, the earth does not possess the gravitational pull that is needed to capture the fast-moving hydrogen atoms.

A detailed check on auroras and magnetic storms has

given up more support for this theory. Some sunspots will persist on the sun's surface longer than the 27 days that is the length of the sun's cycle relative to the earth. The storms and auroras associated with them recur at intervals of 27 days, lagging a day or so behind the sunspot activity. This lag is the time taken by the flying hydrogen atoms to cover the 93 million miles that separate us from the sun. From point to point this twenty-four-hour journey is, therefore, covered at an average speed of about 1000 miles a second.

Although this high-speed hydrogen theory is now widely accepted, it still has difficulties that arouse misgivings. It has been pointed out, for example, that the stream of particles coming from the sun cannot all be positively charged hydrogen atoms. A stream of this sort would disperse as the individual atoms would repel each other.

Scientists have therefore suggested that the stream of positively charged hydrogen atoms sweeps up a corresponding number of negative electrons as it leaves the sun. The jet that travels through space is electrically neutral as a whole, and the individual particles stay close together.

In order to penetrate to within 60 miles of the earth's surface the hydrogen particles must be travelling at tremendous speeds. The overall speed of 1000 miles a second is calculated on a straight-line path between the sun and earth. But in fact the path will be curved, just as a jet of water from a moving hose curves backwards. Also, the influence of the earth's magnetism can cause a moving particle to take a spiral path as it sweeps in towards the pole. The total distance travelled by the particles is thus greater than the 93 million miles that lies between us and the sun. And they must at times be moving faster than 1000 miles a second. Recent estimates have put the particle speed at 2000 miles a second or more. That is to say, in the region of seven million miles an hour.

If this excitation of high-level atmospheric atoms is in fact the cause of the aurora it should be possible to produce an artificial light by firing radio waves into the ionosphere. In 1949 Professor V. A. Bailey, of Sydney University, suggested using an artificial aurora in this way to illuminate a large area at night.

Using a modern atom-splitting machine, physicists of the University of Chicago created a laboratory-scale aurora in 1952. By bombarding the air with fast-moving hydrogen particles and alpha particles they produced a greenish-blue light.

But we are still a long way away from the artificial aurora that will make our street lamps out of date.

15 | Cosmic Rays

RAIN is not the only thing that showers on to us from the atmosphere. Day in, day out, through every season of the year, we live in a storm of flying particles; these particles penetrate our bodies and reach deep down into the earth itself. They are the cosmic rays.

Though scientists have studied these rays intensively during recent years, the cosmic rays remain one of nature's strangest mysteries. We know little of how they are formed; we can only guess where they are coming from. Their very name—cosmic rays—is a confession of our ignorance; they are rays that come from somewhere in the cosmos.

The cosmic rays that reach us on the surface of the earth are different from those that arrive in the upper layers of the atmosphere after travelling through space. They are influenced and changed during their journey through the air. The rays that come from somewhere in space are the primary cosmic rays; those that are formed from the primary rays as they speed through the atmosphere are the secondary rays. It is the secondary rays that reach us on the earth's surface. Both forms of ray consist of tiny particles of matter, smaller than atoms, which travel at tremendous speeds; they are sub-atomic bullets generated by an atomic eruption somewhere in the universe.

Although man has been living in this sub-atomic hailstorm ever since he arrived on earth, it is only during the last half-century that he has known of the existence of the cosmic rays. During the early years of the present century, when physicists were laying the foundations of modern atomic theory, they noticed that the air at ground-level was able to conduct appreciable amounts of electricity. They suspected that this was due to fast-moving sub-atomic particles flying through the air. It is a characteristic of these particles that they are able to make gases conduct electricity.

It was at first believed that the sub-atomic particles in the air were being thrown out by radio-active substances in the earth's crust. But the pioneer British atom scientist C. T. R. Wilson suspected that the rays in the air came, not from the earth, but from some source outside the earth. No matter how well he insulated his laboratory apparatus Wilson found that rays were penetrating the insulation and causing leakage of electricity through the air inside. The particles responsible possessed amazing powers of penetration, far greater than those of any of the sub-atomic bullets emitted by radio-active substances such as radium. Wilson suspected that the rays were reaching the earth from space.

In 1909 a Swiss scientist, A. Gockel, ascended 2½ miles into the air in a balloon and found that the mysterious rays were more active at this height than at ground-level. In the following year an Austrian scientist, Victor Hess, discovered that the rays were even more powerful at a height of 3¼ miles. And in 1913 a German physicist measured the rays at a height of 6 miles; he found that they were 30 times as active as at sea-level. By this time it had become clear that Wilson's suggestion was correct. The rays were indeed coming from outside the earth; the name given to them by Hess, cosmic rays, was accepted.

Since those early days research on cosmic rays has developed steadily; it is now an important part of the world-wide research on atomic physics. Much has been found out about the nature of the particles that form the cosmic rays and the way in which they are influenced as they arrive in the earth's atmosphere.

The cosmic rays that reach ground-level, the secondary rays, are showered on to us in surprising numbers. More than a thousand particles penetrate the human body every minute of the day. The energy brought to the earth by cosmic rays is greater than that reaching us in the light from all the stars, excluding the sun.

The secondary cosmic rays contain several types of particle. Many of the rays are ' soft ' and easily absorbed by matter; they have little power of penetration. Some of the rays, however, are 'hard' and are able to penetrate almost anything that is in their path. These are the rays that embarrassed the physicists in the early days of the present century. The ' hard ' cosmic rays will make their way through many miles of the atmosphere and continue into the earth itself. They have been detected at the bottom of the deepest mines and on the ocean bed still travelling downwards after penetrating thousands of feet of rock or water. Such powers of penetration are quite beyond the capabilities of the more familiar sub-atomic particles, such as those fired off by radio-active substances.

In the classical picture of the atom there is a central core or nucleus, round which small particles circulate in orbits, like planets round the sun. The central nucleus consists of comparatively large particles, including protons, which carry a positive electric charge, and neutrons, which are electrically neutral. These nuclear particles are held tightly together by immensely powerful forces of attraction.

Circulating around this nucleus are the planetary electrons; each electron is only about one two-thousandth as massive as a proton or neutron. These tiny particles carry a negative electrical charge which neutralizes the positive charge given to the nucleus by its protons. The atom as a whole is electrically neutral.

During radio-active decay electrons are fired off, together with alpha particles containing two protons. The alpha rays from radium are the most powerful sub-atomic bullets produced naturally on earth. Yet some cosmic rays are millions of times as energetic as alpha rays. These supremely powerful cosmic-ray particles were identified shortly before World War II as a new form of sub-atomic particle called the meson.

In 1935 the Japanese physicist Yukawa suggested that a particle ought to exist, some 200–300 times as heavy as the electron; it was, said Yukawa, involved in holding together the particles forming the nucleus of the atom. At that time this particle existed only in theory. But in 1937 the American scientist Carl D. Anderson found that such a particle was responsible for the penetrating type of cosmic ray. The new particles were given the name meson.

Inside the atomic nucleus mesons are being constantly created and absorbed. They take part in the interplay of forces that holds the nucleus together, acting as a sort of nuclear glue.

During the 1930's scientists had also been investigating the 'soft' rays. These were found to include tiny electrons possessing only modest powers of penetration. Produced as a result of atomic disruption due to the activity of the primary cosmic rays in the atmosphere, the electrons are released in showers that cascade on to the earth. Measurements made by French Professor Pierre Auger on mountain tops have shown that these cosmic-ray electron showers may cover several square miles of the earth's surface.

In 1942 Anderson discovered that amongst these

showers was a new small particle, the positron, which is a positively-charged counterpart of the electron. Pairs of electrons and positrons are formed by the disintegration of photons, particles of light. These particles, the mesons, electrons, and positrons, were all identified in the secondary cosmic rays. But there still remained the problem of the primary cosmic rays, the rays that enter the atmosphere from space. What sort of particle were they?

By studying the variation in intensity and direction of cosmic rays at different points on the earth's surface scientists concluded that the primary rays were positively-charged sub-atomic particles. And the evidence pointed to the fact that they are almost certainly protons.

By the outbreak of World War II a general picture of cosmic-ray activity had been established. As they reach the earth's atmosphere the protons of the primary cosmic rays disrupt the nuclei of atoms in the gases of the atmosphere. As a result of the atomic explosions, atomic fragments including mesons are formed, together with electrons and positrons which build up into showers as they speed on towards the earth. The mesons are the powerful 'hard' rays; the electrons and positrons are the 'soft' rays.

As research on all aspects of atomic energy intensified during and after the war new facts were discovered about cosmic rays which would not fit easily into this scheme. In 1940 scientists at Aberystwyth University showed that the cosmic ray meson is an unstable particle. It lives for only a small fragment of time before being transformed into other particles. This was as Yukawa had predicted. But the observed life of the cosmic ray meson was, in fact, a hundred times too long to suit Yukawa's theory. The cosmic ray meson, though short-lived, was still living longer than it ought to.

In 1947 Italian physicists found that the cosmic ray meson interacted only weakly with matter. Yet, according to Yukawa, the meson ought to react extremely strongly with the nuclei of atoms in matter. And the difference between the expected and the observed effects was large; one was millions of times the other. It was apparent, therefore, that the cosmic ray meson was not behaving in the manner expected of it.

The solution to this problem came very largely as a result of a new cosmic-ray technique developed at Bristol University by Professor C. Powell and his colleagues. These Bristol scientists found that photographic plates exposed to cosmic rays could be made to show up the tracks of sub-atomic particles formed by the collision between the cosmic rays and atoms inside the photographic emulsion itself. As they sped away from the scene of the atomic disintegration the particles photographed their own tracks on the plate, and by examining these tracks the physicists could study the effects of the atomic explosion.

Using this technique physicists were better able to investigate cosmic-ray activity at great heights in the atmosphere. It has been possible to extend cosmic-ray research into regions where primary rays are colliding with atoms and forming the secondary rays.

When plates were exposed at heights of 10,000 feet in the Andes tracks formed by mesons were traced out in the plates. But it was found that the track of the meson ended abruptly with the formation of another particle. This new particle was identified as a different meson, slightly lighter than the first one.

This discovery has helped to explain the anomalies that existed in cosmic-ray meson behaviour. There are apparently two forms of meson, the first one decaying into the second almost as soon as it had been liberated as a result of the primary ray collision. The first meson behaves in the way predicted by Yukawa. Its life is short, and it acts powerfully on atomic nuclei.

The first-produced mesons are now known as π mesons; as they decay they turn into μ mesons, which are detected at sea-level.

The π meson is 276 times as heavy as an electron. It lives for only a hundred-millionth of a second before turning into the μ meson weighing 210 times as much as an electron.

The mesons carry an electric charge equal to that of an electron; some are positive and some negative. Even with a life of only a few millionths of a second the μ meson is moving so fast that it can travel immense distances. As it decays it produces high-speed electrons and another form of particle called the neutrino.

The primary ray that forms these mesons is rarely able to reach the ground itself. As the fast-moving proton penetrates farther and farther into the atmosphere the odds against its avoiding collision increase rapidly. The atoms of atmospheric gases are packed ever closer together as the height above sea-level diminishes. At 120,000 feet the primary rays are streaming down unchecked; the air is too thin to offer much of a barrier to them. Cosmic rays are a definite hazard to flying at such heights. But at 60,000 feet more than half of the rays have been absorbed.

As collisions take place between the primary rays and the atoms of gas in the atmosphere many of the atomic fragments that are formed are in turn involved in collisions as they speed onward towards the ground. Gradually their energies become spent, and the number and vigour of the flying particles diminishes towards sea-level.

The intensity of cosmic-ray activity therefore reaches a maximum at heights of 60,000–75,000 feet in the atmosphere. Here, primary rays are bombarding the atoms of atmospheric gases, producing new particles in the atomic fragments that are formed. But soon many of these fragments are absorbed and exhausted by the tight-packed atoms in the lower strata of the air.

Above the height of maximum activity the intensity falls off until at 120,000 feet it steadies to nearly a hundred times that at sea-level. This represents the activity of the original rays that are arriving from somewhere in space.

The tendency in modern cosmic-ray research is to reach ever higher into the air in order to study the behaviour of the primary rays and the effects. of their bombardment soon after the atomic explosions have taken place. Cosmic-ray laboratories are perched on mountain tops, like the Jungfraujoch Laboratory 12,000 feet up in the Swiss Alps. From other laboratories equipment is being sent off into the stratosphere behind enormous plastic balloons; even rockets are being brought in to help.

As information accumulates it becomes steadily more apparent that there is much to learn yet about the cosmic-ray process in the atmosphere. Protons are now known to be only one form of the primary cosmic rays. Almost one ray in five is the nucleus of a helium atom. One in every hundred is an even heavier particle. This mixture of atomic particles reaches the earth's atmosphere at a speed approaching that of light.

We do not know where these rays are coming from. Their energies are so enormous that it is not easy to suggest how the rays are formed.

The sun was ruled out as a possible source of cosmic rays when it was found that the rays showered down with undiminished intensity during the night. They appear to reach the earth from all directions. But in 1950 scientists suggested that these facts did not necessarily rule out the sun as a source of cosmic rays.

Particles fired out by the huge solar atomic furnace could circulate for thousands of years in the solar system, striking the earth eventually from many different directions.

Some support for this solar origin of the rays comes from the enormous amount of energy that would be involved if the cosmic rays were distributed throughout space. It would amount to an appreciable proportion of the energy associated with the universe itself.

Whatever the origin of the cosmic rays may be, we can do little to influence our atomic bombardment in any way. It may well be that the cosmic rays play a fundamental role in the progress of human evolution. Radiations of this sort are known to be able to affect the structure of our genes, the hereditary units that pass on characteristics of parents to their offspring. By damaging a gene radiation can cause permanent hereditary changes. It may well be that bombardment by cosmic rays brings about the natural hereditary upsets, or mutations, that appear constantly in human life. They may, therefore, be a major factor in creating the infinite variety of human personality.

So far as any practical applications are concerned it seems unlikely that we shall benefit directly from these showers of energy presented to us gratis by the universe. Although energy carried by individual rays is so immense, the number of rays falling on any area is comparatively small. The amount of energy that could be harnessed from them would be insignificant. Cosmic rays will never generate electricity for us nor make atomic bombs; they cannot run our motor cars nor will they cure the common cold. But they are none the less important for all that. They are giving our physicists a most powerful weapon in their exploration of atomic structure. The cosmic-ray meson carries a punch far greater than that delivered by man-made atom-splitting machines. Collision between a cosmic-ray meson and an atom can have impressive results, enabling the atomic physicist to probe more effectively into the inner workings of the atomic nucleus. With the help they are providing in this way cosmic rays could be a decisive factor in bringing us industrial atomic energy in our time.

Index